# Build up your revision momentum with CGP!

There's a lot to learn for the Edexcel 9-1 International GCSE Physics exams...
it can be tough to get off the starting blocks with your revision.

Not to worry — this brilliant CGP book is packed with Physics tests
that only take ten minutes each.  So you don't have to plough through them
for hours in one session, just fit one in whenever you have a gap in your day.

Every IGCSE Physics topic* is covered, and answers are included at the back.
It's a great way to make sure you're on the right track for the exams!

\* Which includes all the Physics topics from Edexcel's International GCSE Science Double Award.

# CGP — still the best ☺

Our sole aim here at CGP is to produce the highest quality books
— carefully written, immaculately presented and
dangerously close to being funny.

Then we work our socks off to get them out to you
— at the cheapest possible prices.

Published by CGP

Editors:
Sharon Keeley-Holden, Caroline Purvis, Stephen Walters, Sarah Williams

ISBN: 978 1 78908 087 2

With thanks to Karen Wells and Mark Edwards for the proofreading.

Clipart from Corel®
Printed by Elanders Ltd, Newcastle upon Tyne

Based on the classic CGP style created by Richard Parsons.

# Contents

Paper 2

The questions in this book test both Physics Paper 1 and Physics Paper 2 material.  Some material is needed for Paper 2 only — we've marked Paper 2 questions in Sections 1-8 with brackets like this one.

If you're doing a Science (Double Award) qualification you don't need to learn the Paper 2 material.

# Test 1

There are **12 questions** in this test. Give yourself **10 minutes** to answer them all.

Paper 2

1. How does the speed of a car affect its stopping distance at maximum braking force?

    A   The speed of the car doesn't matter.

    B   A greater speed results in a shorter stopping distance.

    C   A greater speed results in a longer stopping distance.

    *[1]*

2. A 4 m long light beam is supported at both ends. A weight is placed on the beam, 1 m from one end. Which of the following statements about the upwards forces provided by the supports is correct?

    A   The support closest to the weight provides a larger force.

    B   The support furthest from the weight provides a larger force.

    C   Both supports provide an equal force.

    *[1]*

3. What is the correct equation to calculate the weight, $W$, of an object of mass $m$ in a gravitational field of strength $g$?

    A   $W = g \div m$

    B   $W = m \times g$

    C   $W = m \div g$

    *[1]*

4. A skydiver has a weight of 750 N. The drag acting upwards on the skydiver is 600 N. What is the resultant vertical force acting on the skydiver?

    A   150 N upwards

    B   150 N downwards

    C   750 N downwards

    *[1]*

5. Which of the following represents distance travelled on a velocity-time graph?

    A   The area under the graph

    B   The gradient of the graph

    C   The highest point on the graph

    *[1]*

6. Two electrically-charged objects exert a force on one another. What is the name given to this type of force?

    A   Gravitational

    B   Electrical

    C   Electrostatic

    *[1]*

7. Which of the following is used as a unit of acceleration?

    A   N/kg

    B   $m/s^2$

    C   m/s

    *[1]*

8. True or False? "If something's moving there must be an overall resultant force on it."

    A   True

    B   False

    *[1]*

**9.** Explain why a vehicle's stopping distance is different to its braking distance.

.......................................................................................................................................

.......................................................................................................................................
*[1]*

**10.** The graph on the right shows how much force must be applied to an elastic object to produce a given extension.

Mark the approximate point on the graph where the relationship between force and extension stops obeying Hooke's Law.

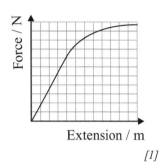

*[1]*

**11.** The graph on the right shows the motion of a unicyclist.

Use the graph to find the average speed of the unicyclist during the first 11 seconds.

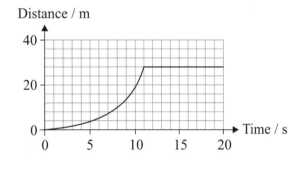

.......................................................................................................................................

.......................................................................................................................................

Speed = ............................ m/s
*[2]*

**12.** A cyclist decelerates from 5.8 m/s to 3.2 m/s in 7 s. The total mass of the cyclist and their bike is 90 kg. What is the average braking force required for this deceleration? Give your answer to two significant figures.

$$F = \frac{mv - mu}{t}$$

.......................................................................................................................................

.......................................................................................................................................

Average braking force = ............................ N

15

*[3]*

Paper 2

# Test 2

There are **10 questions** in this test.  Give yourself **10 minutes** to answer them all.

1.  The acceleration of an object is...

    **A**  ... the change in height over time.

    **B**  ... the change in position over time.

    **C**  ... the change in velocity over time.

    *[1]*

2.  A force has...

    **A**  ... a magnitude but no specific direction.

    **B**  ... a specific direction but no magnitude.

    **C**  ... both a magnitude and a specific direction.

    *[1]*

3.  When a skydiver opens their parachute, their speed decreases because...

    **A**  ... the air resistance acting on them increases.

    **B**  ... the air resistance acting on them decreases.

    **C**  ... their weight decreases.

    *[1]*

4.  For a seesaw starting from rest, if the clockwise moments about the pivot are equal to the anticlockwise moments about it, the seesaw will...

    **A**  ... not turn.

    **B**  ... turn until its centre of mass is below the pivot.

    **C**  ... start turning at a steady speed.

    *[1]*

5.  In an investigation into how the extension of a helical spring varies with the force applied, which of the following is the independent variable?

    **A**  The extension of the spring

    **B**  The force applied to the spring

    **C**  The natural length of the spring

    *[1]*

6.  An object is moving horizontally along a surface.  The object has no driving force acting on it.  Which of the following forces will cause it to slow down?

    **A**  Friction

    **B**  Weight

    **C**  Reaction

    *[1]*

7.  Which of the following pieces of equipment would **not** be needed to investigate the average speed of a toy car?

    **A**  Ruler

    **B**  Mass balance

    **C**  Timing device

    *[1]*

8.  A car accelerates from 9 m/s to 17 m/s in 4 s. What is the average acceleration of the car?

    **A**  2 m/s$^2$

    **B**  8 m/s$^2$

    **C**  32 m/s$^2$

    *[1]*

Paper 2

9. Look at this graph.

   Describe the acceleration of the object between times A and D.

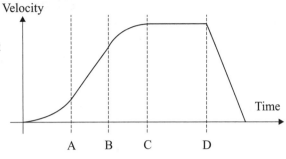

..................................................................................................................................

..................................................................................................................................

..................................................................................................................................

..................................................................................................................................

..................................................................................................................................

[3]

10. Ball A has a mass of 0.70 kg and a momentum of 3.2 kg m/s.
    It collides with Ball B, which is stationary and has a mass of 0.080 kg.
    The balls stick together and move off at a velocity of *v* m/s.

    momentum of Ball A
    = 3.2 kg m/s

    velocity of Ball A and Ball B
    = *v* m/s

    mass of Ball A
    = 0.70 kg

    mass of Ball B
    = 0.080 kg

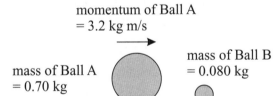

Calculate the final velocity of the balls.

..................................................................................................................................

..................................................................................................................................

..................................................................................................................................

..................................................................................................................................

Velocity = ......................... m/s

[4]

15

Paper 2

6

# Test 3

There are **11 questions** in this test.  Give yourself **10 minutes** to answer them all.

1.  True or False?  "Applying a force can cause an object's speed to change, but not its direction of motion."

    **A**  True

    **B**  False

    *[1]*

2.  How much force would be needed to accelerate a 6 kg object by 3 m/s²?

    **A**  0.5 N

    **B**  2 N

    **C**  18 N

    *[1]*

3.  To travel at a constant speed, the driving force of a car engine must...

    **A**  ... be less than the frictional forces.

    **B**  ... balance the frictional forces.

    **C**  ... exceed the frictional forces.

    *[1]*

4.  The gradient of an object's velocity-time graph gives...

    **A**  ... the distance travelled by the object.

    **B**  ... the maximum velocity of the object.

    **C**  ... the acceleration of the object.

    *[1]*

5.  True or False?  "An object that has been elastically deformed returns to its original shape and length after the deforming force is removed."

    **A**  True

    **B**  False

    *[1]*

6.  Which of these does **not** affect the braking distance of a car?

    **A**  The car's speed

    **B**  The condition of the car's tyres

    **C**  The driver's reaction time

    *[1]*

7.  Which of the following equations correctly shows the relationship between the momentum, $p$, mass, $m$, and velocity, $v$, of a body?

    **A**  $p = m \times v$

    **B**  $p = m \div v$

    **C**  $p = v \div m$

    *[1]*

Paper 2

8.  A ball hits a wall with a force of 5 N.  What is the force exerted on the ball by the wall?

    **A**  0 N

    **B**  −5 N

    **C**  − 10 N

    *[1]*

Paper 2

---

Section 1 — Forces and Motion

**9.** Calculate the weight of a man with a mass of 83 kg.
Assume the Earth's gravitational field strength is 10 N/kg.

.........................................................................................................................................

Weight = ............................. N

*[1]*

**10.** Calculate the magnitude of the resultant force acting on the block
shown in the diagram below.

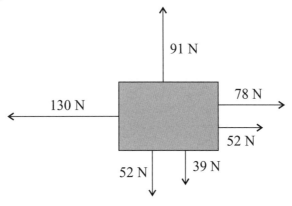

.........................................................................................................................................

.........................................................................................................................................

Resultant force = ....................................... N

*[3]*

**11.** A car is travelling at a speed of 13 m/s. The driver applies the brakes and the car comes
to rest after travelling a further 26 m. What is the deceleration of the car?

$(\text{final speed})^2 = (\text{initial speed})^2 + (2 \times \text{acceleration} \times \text{distance moved})$

.........................................................................................................................................

.........................................................................................................................................

.........................................................................................................................................

Deceleration = ............................ m/s²

*[3]*

15

# Test 4

There are **10 questions** in this test.  Give yourself **10 minutes** to answer them all.

1. A force is applied to a trolley and causes an acceleration of 2.4 m/s². The same force is applied to a second trolley with half the mass of the first. What will the acceleration of the second trolley be?

   A   1.2 m/s²

   B   2.4 m/s²

   C   4.8 m/s²

   *[1]*

2. The extension of a stretched spring that is obeying Hooke's law is...

   A   ... directly proportional to the force applied.

   B   ... inversely proportional to the force applied.

   C   ... unrelated to the force applied.

   *[1]*

3. Which of the following forces only acts between bodies that are in contact with one another?

   A   Gravitational force

   B   Friction

   C   Electrostatic force

   *[1]*

4. A cyclist travels at 4.5 m/s for 6.0 s. How far does he move in this time?

   A   1.3 m

   B   10.5 m

   C   27 m

   *[1]*

5. What does a horizontal line on an object's distance-time graph indicate about the motion of the object?

   A   The object is moving at constant speed.

   B   The object is stationary.

   C   The object is accelerating.

   *[1]*

6. A force of 45 N east, a force of 60 N east and a force of 85 N west act on an object. What is the resultant force on the object?

   A   190 N east

   B   20 N east

   C   20 N west

   *[1]*

7. A force acting on a body will **not** change the body's...

   A   ... total mass.

   B   ... direction of motion.

   C   ... shape.

   *[1]*

Paper 2

8. Car safety features are designed to...

   A   ... decrease the time taken for a passenger's momentum to change.

   B   ... increase the time taken for a passenger's momentum to change.

   *[1]*

---

Section 1 — Forces and Motion

9. Explain how and why an object's speed changes as it falls through a fluid from rest to a terminal velocity.

..............................................................................................................................................

..............................................................................................................................................

..............................................................................................................................................

..............................................................................................................................................

*[3]*

10. A uniform 8.0 m rod weighing 1500 N is suspended horizontally at rest. The rod is attached to a pivot at one end, and supported by a vertical rope at the other, as shown in the diagram.

Find the upwards force applied to the rod by the rope.

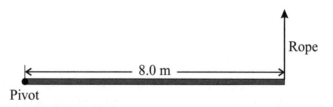

Rope

8.0 m

Pivot

..............................................................................................................................................

..............................................................................................................................................

..............................................................................................................................................

..............................................................................................................................................

Force = ........................... N

*[4]*

15

# Test 5

There are **11 questions** in this test. Give yourself **10 minutes** to answer them all.

1. True or False? "The resistance of a thermistor increases, as temperature increases."

   **A**   True

   **B**   False

   *[1]*

2. What is the unit of power?

   **A**   Joule, J

   **B**   Ohm, Ω

   **C**   Watt, W

   *[1]*

3. True or False? "Two components connected in parallel will each have the same voltage across them."

   **A**   True

   **B**   False

   *[1]*

4. A circuit has a power source with a fixed voltage. What happens to the current if you increase the resistance in this circuit?

   **A**   The current would increase.

   **B**   The current would stay the same.

   **C**   The current would decrease.

   *[1]*

5. A 2 Ω resistor in a circuit has a 4 A current through it. What is the voltage across the resistor?

   **A**   2 V

   **B**   0.5 V

   **C**   8 V

   *[1]*

6. True or False? "Earthing the metal casing of an appliance will prevent large currents from flowing if a fault occurs."

   **A**   True

   **B**   False

   *[1]*

7. Whilst refuelling an aircraft, the fuel hose may gain electrostatic charge. Why is this potentially dangerous?

   **A**   The hose will become live.

   **B**   It could cause a spark, igniting the fuel.

   **C**   It could cause the hose to become blocked.

   *[1]*

8. Polystyrene gains electrostatic charge when it's rubbed against fabric. This results from the movement of which type of particle?

   **A**   Electrons

   **B**   Neutrons

   **C**   Protons

   *[1]*

Paper 2

    

**9.** Most electrical appliances have a fuse connected to their live wire.
Describe how a fuse ensures an appliance doesn't become unsafe in the case of a fault.

...................................................................................................................................................

...................................................................................................................................................

*[1]*

**10.** While in use, a 1.2 V cell transfers 5.4 kJ of energy.
How much charge passed through the cell in this time?

...................................................................................................................................................

...................................................................................................................................................

...................................................................................................................................................

Charge = ........................... C

*[3]*

**11.** The current-voltage graph of a filament lamp
is shown on the right.

Explain why the graph curves as the current increases.

...................................................................................................................................................

...................................................................................................................................................

...................................................................................................................................................

...................................................................................................................................................

*[3]*

15

# Test 6

There are **11 questions** in this test. Give yourself **10 minutes** to answer them all.

1. True or False? "It is not necessary to earth a double insulated appliance."

   A True

   B False

   [1]

2. True or False? "In a series circuit, the voltage of the power supply is shared between all components."

   A True

   B False

   [1]

3. Electric current is...

   A ... the driving force that pushes charges around a circuit.

   B ... a measure of how much charges slow down as they flow through a circuit.

   C ... the rate of flow of charge.

   [1]

4. What causes the wire inside a filament bulb to heat up when electrical charge flows through it?

   A Earthing

   B Insulation

   C Resistance

   [1]

5. A current of 0.2 A passes through an electric motor over a period of 3 minutes. What is the total charge transferred through the motor in this time?

   A 9.0 C

   B 36 C

   C 900 C

   [1]

6. Two resistors are connected in series with a power supply. Which of the following changes will increase current in the circuit?

   A Removing one of the resistors.

   B Adding a third resistor in series.

   C Decreasing the voltage of the power supply.

   [1]

7. Cars' headlights are connected in parallel. What is the advantage of this arrangement?

   A The headlights will not become live.

   B It will save battery life.

   C If one headlight breaks, the other will not be affected.

   [1]

8. Inkjet printers produce positively charged ink droplets. The droplets pass between charged plates. They are attracted towards...

   A ... the positively charged plate.

   B ... the negatively charged plate.

   C ... the uncharged plate.

   [1]

Paper 2

---

Section 2 — Electricity

**9.** Hair straighteners with a power of 150 W are plugged into a 230 V mains supply. Calculate the current through the hair straighteners.

......................................................................................................................

......................................................................................................................

......................................................................................................................

......................................................................................................................

Current = ..................... A

*[3]*

**10.** A student rubs a balloon against their hair, causing the balloon to gain a negative charge. Explain why the student's hair stands on end when the balloon is held above their head.

......................................................................................................................

......................................................................................................................

......................................................................................................................

......................................................................................................................

......................................................................................................................

*[3]*

Paper 2

**11.** State what happens to the particles in the copper strip when the power supply is switched on and the bulb lights up.

copper strip

......................................................................................................................

......................................................................................................................

......................................................................................................................

*[1]*

15

14

# Test 7

There are **11 questions** in this test. Give yourself **10 minutes** to answer them all.

1. True or False? "The UK mains electricity supply is direct current."

   **A**   True

   **B**   False

   *[1]*

2. True or False? "An ammeter must be connected in parallel with a component to measure the current through the component."

   **A**   True

   **B**   False

   *[1]*

3. A current is flowing through a diode in a circuit. How would the current flowing change if the direction of the applied voltage was reversed?

   **A**   The current would not change.

   **B**   The current would not flow any more.

   **C**   The current would increase.

   *[1]*

4. Resistors A and B are connected in series with a power supply. Resistor A has a resistance of 3 Ω. Resistor B has a resistance of 9 Ω. What is the total resistance in the circuit?

   **A**   6 Ω

   **B**   3 Ω

   **C**   12 Ω

   *[1]*

5. A 0.5 A and a 1.5 A current flow into a junction. Current leaves the junction through one wire. What is the current in this wire?

   **A**   1 A

   **B**   2 A

   **C**   3 A

   *[1]*

6. Components connected in parallel to a power supply will usually receive...

   **A**   ... a fraction of the voltage of the power source.

   **B**   ... the same current as any other component in the circuit.

   **C**   ... the full voltage of the power source.

   *[1]*

7. What is the correct definition of voltage?

   **A**   Energy transferred per unit charge passed.

   **B**   The rate of flow of charge.

   **C**   The rate at which energy is transferred.

   *[1]*

8. Which of the following devices makes use of electrostatic charges?

   **A**   Fuelling hoses

   **B**   Plotting compass

   **C**   Photocopier

   *[1]*

Paper 2

---

Section 2 — Electricity

© CGP — not to be photocopied

**9.** A 16 V power supply, a 40 Ω resistor and an ammeter are connected in series. Calculate the size of the current measured by the ammeter.

16 V

40 Ω    A

..................................................................................................

..................................................................................................

..................................................................................................

Current = ........................... A

*[2]*

**10.** Explain why a resistor typically heats up as current flows through it.

..................................................................................................

..................................................................................................

..................................................................................................

..................................................................................................

*[2]*

**11.** 1 062 600 J of energy was transferred by an electric welder drawing a current of 11 A from a 230 V mains electricity supply. Calculate the length of time the iron was used for. Use the following equation:

Energy transferred = current × voltage × time

..................................................................................................

..................................................................................................

..................................................................................................

..................................................................................................

Time = ................................ s

*[3]*

15

## Test 8

There are **11 questions** in this test. Give yourself **10 minutes** to answer them all.

1.  The different types of electromagnetic waves...

    A   ... all have the same wavelength.

    B   ... all have the same frequency.

    C   ... form a continuous spectrum.

    *[1]*

2.  What is the 'normal' on a ray diagram?

    A   A line drawn to connect the incident and emerging rays.

    B   A line drawn perpendicular to a surface at the point of incidence.

    C   A line drawn to show the critical angle.

    *[1]*

3.  A light ray travels through ice. The critical angle for the light ray hitting a boundary between the ice and air is 50.0°. The refractive index of ice is...

    A   1.3

    B   0.77

    C   1.1

    *[1]*

4.  A source moving towards an observer emits a wave. The wavelength of the wave observed will appear shorter than the wavelength of the wave emitted. This effect is called...

    A   ... the Doppler effect.

    B   ... refraction.

    C   ... total internal reflection.

    *[1]*

5.  The speed of sound in air is about 340 m/s. What is the approximate wavelength of a sound wave with a frequency of 850 Hz?

    A   2.5 m

    B   0.40 m

    C   290 000 m

    *[1]*

6.  The amplitude of a wave is...

    A   ... the length of a full cycle of the wave.

    B   ... the number of complete cycles of the wave passing a point per second.

    C   ... the maximum displacement from the rest position, e.g. to a crest or a trough.

    *[1]*

7.  Which of the following is correct?

    A   Only transverse waves can be refracted.

    B   Only electromagnetic waves can be refracted.

    C   Any wave can be refracted.

    *[1]*

8.  True or False? "A typical human can hear a sound with a frequency of 30 kHz."

    A   True

    B   False

    *[1]*

Paper 2

9. The diagram below shows the different regions of the electromagnetic spectrum and their wavelengths, $\lambda$. Name the regions labelled **A** and **D** in the diagram below.

| Region | Radio waves | A | B | Visible light | C | D | Gamma rays |
|--------|-------------|---|---|---------------|---|---|------------|
| $\lambda$ (m) | $1-10^4$ m | $10^{-2}$ m | $10^{-5}$ m | $10^{-7}$ m | $10^{-8}$ m | $10^{-10}$ m | $10^{-15}$ m |

A: ...................................................  D: .........................................................

*[2]*

10. Give **two** different uses of infrared radiation.

1. ...........................................................................................................................

2. ...........................................................................................................................

*[2]*

11. Describe how the apparatus shown below can be used to measure the speed of sound in air.

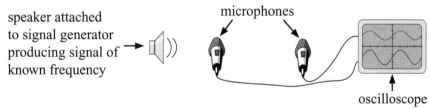

speaker attached to signal generator producing signal of known frequency

microphones

oscilloscope

..........................................................................................................................

..........................................................................................................................

..........................................................................................................................

..........................................................................................................................

..........................................................................................................................

*[3]*

15

Section 3 — Waves

Paper 2

# Test 9

There are **11 questions** in this test.  Give yourself **10 minutes** to answer them all.

1.  A light ray travelling through a transparent block hits the boundary between the block and air.  The critical angle is determined by...

    **A**   ... the shape of the block.

    **B**   ... the angle of incidence of the ray.

    **C**   ... the material the block is made from.

    *[1]*

2.  Which of the following is **not** true for light waves?

    **A**   They are transverse waves.

    **B**   They are longitudinal waves.

    **C**   They are part of the electromagnetic spectrum.

    *[1]*

3.  True or False?  "Waves transfer matter."

    **A**   True

    **B**   False

    *[1]*

4.  True or False?  "The angle of incidence is equal to the angle of reflection."

    **A**   True

    **B**   False

    *[1]*

5.  10 complete wave cycles pass a point in 2 seconds.  Which statement below is true?

    **A**   The period of the wave is 0.2 s.

    **B**   The period of the wave is 5 s.

    **C**   The frequency of the wave is 0.2 s.

    *[1]*

6.  A light ray hits the boundary between water and air at the critical angle.  This means that the angle of refraction is...

    **A**   ... greater than 90°.

    **B**   ... the same as the angle of incidence.

    **C**   ... 90°.

    *[1]*

7.  Which of the following statements about electromagnetic (EM) waves is correct?

    **A**   All EM waves travel through free space at the same speed.

    **B**   The higher the frequency of an EM wave, the faster it travels through free space.

    **C**   The higher the frequency of an EM wave, the slower it travels through free space.

    *[1]*

8.  Why does the frequency of a sound wave appear to increase when its source starts moving towards you?

    **A**   The wavefronts in front of the source spread out.

    **B**   The wavefronts in front of the source get closer together.

    **C**   The sound waves travel a shorter distance.

    *[1]*

---

Section 3 — Waves

**9.** A light ray enters a block at an angle to the normal, as shown on the diagram below. The refractive index of the block is higher than that of air.
Continue the light ray on the diagram to show how it may refract when it enters the block. Then continue the light ray further to show it leaving the block.

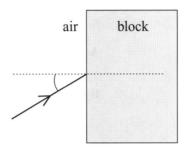

*[2]*

**10.** Calculate the speed of a wave with a frequency of $3.0 \times 10^7$ Hz and a wavelength of 1.4 m.

...................................................................................................................................

...................................................................................................................................

...................................................................................................................................

Wave speed = ............................. m/s
*[3]*

**11.** The wave traces of two sounds, A and B, are shown on the right.

State one similarity and one difference that an observer would notice between sounds A and B.

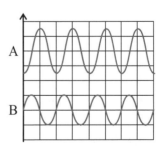

Similarity: ..................................................................................................

Difference: ..................................................................................................
*[2]*

15

Paper 2

# Test 10

There are **11 questions** in this test. Give yourself **10 minutes** to answer them all.

1.  What units are used for wave speed?

    **A**  Metres, m.

    **B**  Metres per second, m/s.

    **C**  Hertz, Hz.

    *[1]*

2.  In a longitudinal wave, the vibrations are...

    **A**  ... parallel to the direction of energy transfer.

    **B**  ... perpendicular to the direction of energy transfer.

    *[1]*

3.  A ray diagram illustrating a light ray refracting will show the ray...

    **A**  ... spreading out as it hits a new medium.

    **B**  ... changing direction as it enters a new medium.

    **C**  ... transferring its energy to the medium as it enters that new medium.

    *[1]*

4.  What is the frequency of a wave?

    **A**  The number of waves passing a point per second.

    **B**  The distance travelled by the wave each second.

    **C**  The distance from one crest on a wave to the next adjacent crest.

    *[1]*

5.  Which of the following has the shortest wavelength?

    **A**  Microwaves

    **B**  Infrared

    **C**  Ultraviolet

    *[1]*

6.  Which of the following leads to total internal reflection?

    **A**  angle of incidence = critical angle

    **B**  angle of incidence > critical angle

    **C**  angle of incidence < critical angle

    *[1]*

7.  What is the range of human hearing?

    **A**  0 - 2000 Hz

    **B**  20 - 20 000 Hz

    **C**  2000 - 200 000 Hz

    *[1]*

8.  Which of the following relies on the total internal reflection of light?

    **A**  The transmission of information along optical fibres.

    **B**  The transmission of information between satellites.

    **C**  The focussing of light rays in a camera.

    *[1]*

Paper 2

---

Section 3 — Waves

© CGP — not to be photocopied

9.  Name **two** types of electromagnetic radiation that can
    cause harm.  State a potential harmful effect of each one.

    1. Type of radiation: ...................................................................................................................

       Harmful effect: ......................................................................................................................

    2. Type of radiation: ...................................................................................................................

       Harmful effect: ......................................................................................................................

    *[2]*

10. A signal generator is being used to produce waves in a ripple tank.  The signal generator
    is set to 4 Hz.  How long does a full wave take to pass a point marked on the ripple tank?

    $$\text{frequency} = \frac{1}{\text{time period}}$$

    ................................................................................................................................................

    ................................................................................................................................................

    Length of time = .............................. s

    *[2]*

11. A student is investigating the refractive index of a glass block.
    He directs a ray of light through the block and traces its path, as shown below.

    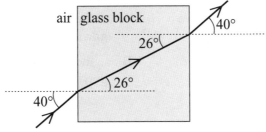

    Use information from the diagram to calculate the refractive index of glass.
    Give your answer to two significant figures.

    ................................................................................................................................................

    ................................................................................................................................................

    Refractive index = .............................

    *[3]*

15

# Section 4 — Energy Resources and Energy Transfer

# Test 11

There are **11 questions** in this test. Give yourself **10 minutes** to answer them all.

1. True or False? "Energy can be created but not destroyed."

   **A**  True

   **B**  False

   *[1]*

2. An object that is hotter than its surroundings will...

   **A**  ... emit more radiation than it absorbs.

   **B**  ... absorb more radiation than it emits.

   **C**  ... will not absorb radiation.

   *[1]*

3. Hot air rises above cold air in a room. This is because the density of the hot air is...

   **A**  ... higher than the density of the cold air.

   **B**  ... equal to the density of the cold air.

   **C**  ... lower than the density of the cold air.

   *[1]*

4. Power is the...

   **A**  ... conservation of momentum.

   **B**  ... energy of a moving object.

   **C**  ... rate of doing work.

   *[1]*

5. What happens to the amount of energy in a car's kinetic energy store when the car slows down?

   **A**  It remains the same.

   **B**  It decreases as some energy is transferred away to different energy stores.

   **C**  It decreases as some energy is destroyed.

   *[1]*

6. When an object falls from a height, the maximum energy transferred to its kinetic energy store is equal to...

   **A**  ... the energy transferred away from its gravitational potential energy store.

   **B**  ... the energy transferred to its gravitational potential energy store.

   *[1]*

7. 800 J of energy is supplied to a toaster with an efficiency of 25%. How much energy is transferred usefully by the toaster?

   **A**  200 J

   **B**  775 J

   **C**  1000 J

   *[1]*

8. Fossil fuels can be used to generate electricity. In which of the following is energy stored in fossil fuels?

   **A**  kinetic energy stores

   **B**  chemical energy stores

   **C**  thermal energy stores

   *[1]*

Paper 2

9. Suggest two environmental disadvantages of using tidal-powered turbines to generate electricity.

1. ........................................................................................................................

........................................................................................................................

2. ........................................................................................................................

........................................................................................................................

[2]

10. A race car travels along a straight length of track at 65 m/s.
The race car and its driver have a combined mass of 580 kg.
Calculate the total energy in the kinetic energy stores of the race car and driver.

........................................................................................................................

........................................................................................................................

Energy = ........................... J

[2]

11. A lorry has 1 417 500 J of energy in its kinetic energy store.
The brakes are applied and do work to bring the lorry to rest.
The brakes apply a constant braking force 56 000 N.
Calculate the total distance travelled by the lorry while the brakes are being applied.

........................................................................................................................

........................................................................................................................

........................................................................................................................

........................................................................................................................

Braking distance = ............................... m

[3]

15

# Test 12

There are **10 questions** in this test. Give yourself **10 minutes** to answer them all.

1. True or False? "If a moving object doubles its speed, it doubles the energy in its kinetic energy store."

   A   True

   B   False

   *[1]*

2. How much work is done when a crate weighing 1200 N is lifted 4 m into the air?

   A   300 J

   B   2400 J

   C   4800 J

   *[1]*

3. Energy can only be transferred by convection in...

   A   ... solids.

   B   ... liquids.

   C   ... liquids and gases.

   *[1]*

4. The amount of energy transferred by an appliance depends on...

   A   ... its power and size.

   B   ... its power and the time it is on for.

   C   ... its power and mass.

   *[1]*

5. When a rock rolls down a hill, some energy in its gravitational potential energy store is transferred to other stores. Which of these stores is energy **not** transferred to?

   A   The rock's kinetic energy store.

   B   The rock's chemical energy store.

   C   The thermal energy store of the surroundings.

   *[1]*

6. 250 J of energy is supplied to a fan. The fan transfers 100 J of this energy to useful energy stores. What is the efficiency of the fan?

   A   10%

   B   40%

   C   60%

   *[1]*

7. True or False? "Work done is equal to energy transferred."

   A   True

   B   False

   *[1]*

8. Which of these is a disadvantage of using solar cells to generate electricity?

   A   Their reliability depends on the weather.

   B   They produce $CO_2$ when running.

   C   They pose a danger to birds.

   *[1]*

Paper 2

Section 4 — Energy Resources and Energy Transfer

© CGP — not to be photocopied

**9.** A 500 g object falls off a cliff and loses 100 J from its gravitational potential energy store. If the gravitational field strength, $g = 10$ N/kg, how high is the cliff?

.................................................................................................................................

.................................................................................................................................

.................................................................................................................................

Height = ............................... m

*[3]*

**10.** The diagram below shows a Leslie cube. A Leslie cube is a hollow metal cube that can be filled with water. It has four vertical faces. Each face is made from the same material, but they have different colours and textures.

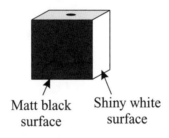

Matt black
surface

Shiny white
surface

Describe a method that can be used to compare the amount of radiation emitted from the cube's matt black face to the amount emitted from its shiny white face. In your description, include how to make the investigation fair.

.................................................................................................................................

.................................................................................................................................

.................................................................................................................................

.................................................................................................................................

.................................................................................................................................

.................................................................................................................................

.................................................................................................................................

*[4]*

15

# Test 13

There are **11 questions** in this test.  Give yourself **10 minutes** to answer them all.

**1.** What would happen to the Earth's temperature if the atmosphere was absorbing more radiation than it was emitting?

   **A**   It would increase.

   **B**   It would decrease.

*[1]*

**2.** True or False? "A convection current in a liquid is caused by density changes in the liquid as its temperature changes."

   **A**   True

   **B**   False

*[1]*

**3.** What is the correct equation for calculating the amount of energy in an object's kinetic energy store?

   **A**   $KE = \frac{1}{2} \times m \times v$

   **B**   $KE = 2 \times m \times v$

   **C**   $KE = \frac{1}{2} \times m \times v^2$

*[1]*

**4.** A force $F$ does work $W$ to push a box a distance 2 m across a floor.  To push the box 4 m using the same force...

   **A**   ... $0.5 \times W$ work would need to be done.

   **B**   ... $2 \times W$ work would need to be done.

   **C**   ... $4 \times W$ work would need to be done.

*[1]*

**5.** What is the power of a device that transfers 20 J in five seconds?

   **A**   4 W

   **B**   20 W

   **C**   100 W

*[1]*

**6.** True or False? "One advantage of using renewable resources to generate electricity is that these resources won't run out."

Paper 2

   **A**   True

   **B**   False

*[1]*

**7.** In a geothermal power station, steam is used to generate electricity.  Energy in the kinetic energy store of the steam is transferred to...

Paper 2

   **A**   ... the nuclear energy store of a generator.

   **B**   ... the chemical energy store of a generator.

   **C**   ... the kinetic energy store of a turbine.

*[1]*

**8.** When a racket hits a ball, energy is transferred from the racket's kinetic energy store to the ball's kinetic energy store. This energy is transferred...

   **A**   ... by heating.

   **B**   ... mechanically.

   **C**   ... electrically.

*[1]*

**9.** Give the **two** energy stores that energy is usefully transferred to in a hairdryer.

1. .................................................................................................................................

2. .................................................................................................................................

*[1]*

**10.** A 70 kg skydiver jumps out of an aeroplane and falls a height of 4000 metres. Calculate the amount of energy lost from her gravitational potential energy store. $g = 10$ N/kg

.................................................................................................................................

.................................................................................................................................

.................................................................................................................................

Energy = ............................ J

*[3]*

**11.** The Sankey diagram below shows the energy transfers in a motor.

Calculate the amount of energy usefully transferred and the efficiency of the motor as a percentage.

.................................................................................................................................

.................................................................................................................................

.................................................................................................................................

Energy usefully transferred = ........................ J

Efficiency = ........................ %

*[3]*

# Test 14

There are **11 questions** in this test.  Give yourself **10 minutes** to answer them all.

1.  True or False?  "The amount of energy wasted in a system is always equal to the amount of energy destroyed."

    **A**  True

    **B**  False

    *[1]*

2.  30 J of work is done to heat a bowl of soup. How much energy was transferred?

    **A**  0 J

    **B**  3 J

    **C**  30 J

    *[1]*

3.  True or False?  "Thermal conduction is where particles collide with each other and transfer energy between their kinetic energy stores."

    **A**  True

    **B**  False

    *[1]*

4.  Which of the following is **not** an energy transfer?

    **A**  Sound

    **B**  Light

    **C**  Gravity

    *[1]*

5.  Which of these statements is false?

    **A**  When an object falls, work is done against gravity.

    **B**  When an object falls, energy is lost from its gravitational potential energy store.

    **C**  When an object is lifted, work is done against gravity.

    *[1]*

6.  An apple with a mass of 0.1 kg hangs 2 m above the ground.  Assuming the gravitational field strength is 10 N/kg, how much energy will the apple lose from its gravitational potential energy store if it falls to the ground?

    **A**  0.5 J

    **B**  2 J

    **C**  5 J

    *[1]*

7.  5000 J of energy was supplied to an electric motor with an efficiency of 68%.  How much energy was usefully transferred by the motor?

    **A**  5000 J

    **B**  3400 J

    **C**  1600 J

    *[1]*

8.  Which of the following can be done to reduce an unwanted energy transfer from an object's thermal energy store to the thermal energy stores of its surroundings?

    **A**  Lubricate the object.

    **B**  Heat the object.

    **C**  Insulate the object.

    *[1]*

---

Section 4 — Energy Resources and Energy Transfer

**9.** Solar cells can be used to generate electricity. How is energy transferred to a solar cell?

...................................................................................................................................................

*[1]*

**10.** A robot has a power output of 50 W. How much energy does it transfer in 2 minutes?

...................................................................................................................................................

...................................................................................................................................................

Energy = ........................... J

*[2]*

**11.** A 0.080 kg pinball sits at rest on a compressed spring. The spring has 7.0 J of energy in its elastic potential energy store. The spring is released and transfers all of this energy to the pinball as shown in the Sankey diagram below.

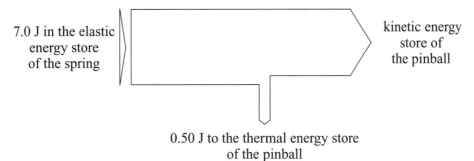

7.0 J in the elastic energy store of the spring

kinetic energy store of the pinball

0.50 J to the thermal energy store of the pinball

Calculate the speed the pinball leaves the spring.
Give your answer to two significant figures.

...................................................................................................................................................

...................................................................................................................................................

...................................................................................................................................................

Speed = ........................... m/s

*[4]*

15

# Test 15

There are **10 questions** in this test.  Give yourself **10 minutes** to answer them all.

1.  Which of these temperatures on the Celsius scale is known as absolute zero?

    **A**   –273 °C

    **B**   –237 °C

    **C**   0 °C

    *[1]*

2.  In a gas or liquid at rest, the pressure at a point acts...

    **A**   ... in one direction only.

    **B**   ... equally in all directions.

    **C**   ... towards Earth only.

    *[1]*

3   A force of 15 N acts over an area of 0.3 m². What is the pressure exerted by the force?

    **A**   4.5 Pa

    **B**   30 Pa

    **C**   50 Pa

    *[1]*

4.  What will happen to the pressure of a fixed volume of gas if its temperature is increased?

    **A**   It will decrease

    **B**   It will increase

    **C**   It will stay the same

    *[1]*

5.  What happens to the temperature of an ice cube as it melts into water?

    **A**   It stays the same

    **B**   It increases

    **C**   It decreases

    *[1]*

6.  Which equation is used to calculate the pressure difference between two points in a gas of density $\rho$?  (Height difference between points = $h$, gravitational field strength = $g$.)

    **A**   pressure difference = $h \times \rho \times g$

    **B**   pressure difference = $h \times \rho \div g$

    **C**   pressure difference = $h \div \rho \times g$

    *[1]*

7.  What is the specific heat capacity of a substance?

    **A**   The energy released by a substance when it freezes.

    **B**   The total energy stored by the particles in a system.

    **C**   The energy needed to raise the temperature of 1 kg of a substance by 1 °C.

    *[1]*

8.  Why does the average speed of the particles in a gas increase if the temperature of the gas is increased?

    **A**   The particles collide with one another less often at higher temperatures.

    **B**   The amount of energy in the particles' kinetic energy stores increases with temperature.

    **C**   The mass of the particles decreases with temperature.

    *[1]*

Paper 2

Paper 2

9.  A sealed container with a moveable lid is filled with gas. The gas is compressed so that it has a volume of 290 cm³. The gas has a pressure of 160 kPa. The gas is then allowed to expand until its pressure reaches 110 kPa. If the temperature of the gas remains constant, calculate the new volume of the gas in cm³.

$$P_1 V_1 = P_2 V_2$$

Where $P_1$ is the pressure at volume $V_1$, and $P_2$ is the pressure at volume $V_2$.

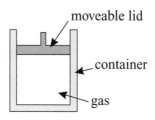

moveable lid

container

gas

.........................................................................................................................

.........................................................................................................................

.........................................................................................................................

Volume = ............................................. cm³

*[3]*

10. The cube below has a density of 8800 kg/m³. Calculate the mass of the cube.

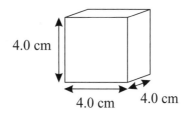

4.0 cm

4.0 cm          4.0 cm

.........................................................................................................................

.........................................................................................................................

.........................................................................................................................

.........................................................................................................................

.........................................................................................................................

Mass = ............................ kg

*[4]*

15

Section 5 — Solids, Liquids and Gases

# Test 16

There are **11 questions** in this test. Give yourself **10 minutes** to answer them all.

Paper 2

**1.** Which of the following is **not** caused by heating a liquid?

   **A**  The energy in the particles' kinetic energy stores increasing.

   **B**  The distance between the particles increasing.

   **C**  The arrangement of the particles becoming more regular.

*[1]*

**2.** Absolute zero is the temperature at which...

   **A**  ... the temperature in kelvin is equal to the temperature in Celsius.

   **B**  ... particles have as little energy in their kinetic energy stores as it is possible to have.

   **C**  ... water freezes into ice.

*[1]*

**3.** Which is the correct equation for density?

   **A**  density = mass × volume

   **B**  density = volume ÷ mass

   **C**  density = mass ÷ volume

*[1]*

**4.** What is 25 °C in kelvin?

   **A**  −248 K

   **B**  25 K

   **C**  298 K

*[1]*

**5.** Which of the following correctly describes the motion of particles in a gas?

   **A**  The particles travel in random directions at a range of speeds.

   **B**  The particles vibrate about fixed positions.

   **C**  The particles travel in random directions at a single, fixed speed.

*[1]*

**6.** What happens to the pressure of a gas held at constant temperature when the volume it occupies decreases?

   **A**  It increases

   **B**  It decreases

   **C**  It stays the same

*[1]*

**7.** A pressure of 2.0 Pa acts on a hydraulic piston with an area of 2.4 m². What is the force applied to the hydraulic piston?

   **A**  1.2 N

   **B**  4.8 N

   **C**  9.6 N

*[1]*

**8.** If the Kelvin temperature of a gas is doubled, what happens to the average energy in the kinetic energy stores of its particles?

   **A**  It stays the same.

   **B**  It halves.

   **C**  It doubles.

*[1]*

9.  A gas is in a rigid, sealed container. The amount of energy in the kinetic energy stores of
    its particles increases. Explain why the pressure of the gas increases.

    .........................................................................................................................................

    .........................................................................................................................................

    .........................................................................................................................................
    *[2]*


10. A barrel with a height of 0.82 m is filled to the top with crude oil.
    Calculate the pressure due to the oil at a point at the bottom of the barrel.
    Crude oil has a density of 870 kg/m³.
    The gravitational field strength of the Earth is 10 N/kg.

    .........................................................................................................................................

    .........................................................................................................................................

    .........................................................................................................................................

    Pressure at bottom of barrel due to oil = ........................................ Pa
    *[3]*


11. The specific heat capacity of copper is 390 J/kg°C.

    Calculate the amount of energy needed to increase
    the temperature of 500 g of copper by 15 °C.

    change in thermal energy = mass × specific heat capacity × temperature change

    .........................................................................................................................................

    .........................................................................................................................................

    .........................................................................................................................................

    Energy = ........................................ J
    *[2]*

Section 5 — Solids, Liquids and Gases

15

Paper 2

# Test 17

There are **11 questions** in this test.  Give yourself **10 minutes** to answer them all.

1.  If an electrical conductor moves through a magnetic field...

    **A**   ... the magnetic field disappears.

    **B**   ... the magnetic field reverses.

    **C**   ... a voltage is induced in the conductor.

    *[1]*

2.  When placed near a bar magnet, what does a plotting compass tell you about the magnetic field at that point?

    **A**   Only its strength.

    **B**   Only its direction.

    **C**   Both its strength and direction.

    *[1]*

3.  True or False?  "Reversing the direction of rotation of a coil of wire in a magnetic field affects the size of the voltage induced in the coil."

    **A**   True

    **B**   False

    *[1]*

4.  Induced magnets produce a magnetic field...

    **A**   ... all the time.

    **B**   ... only if they experience a change in electric field.

    **C**   ... only while they are in another magnetic field.

    *[1]*

5.  A current-carrying wire placed between the poles of a magnet experiences a force because...

    **A**   ... its magnetic field interacts with the magnetic field between the poles.

    **B**   ... the magnetic field between the poles stops the flow of current in the wire.

    **C**   ... a voltage is induced between the magnetic poles.

    *[1]*

6.  Which of the following are attracted to the north pole of a permanent magnet?

    **A**   Magnetic materials and the north poles of other permanent magnets

    **B**   Magnetic materials and the south poles of other permanent magnets

    **C**   The south poles of other permanent magnets only

    *[1]*

7.  A charged particle in a magnetic field won't feel a force if its direction of motion is...

    **A**   ... parallel to the magnetic field.

    **B**   ... at 45° to the magnetic field.

    **C**   ... perpendicular to the magnetic field.

    *[1]*

8.  The magnetic field produced when current flows through a wire...

    **A**   ... is parallel to the wire.

    **B**   ... is only at each end of the wire.

    **C**   ... goes round the wire in circles centred on the wire.

    *[1]*

Paper 2

Paper 2

9.  In which direction will this coil turn, clockwise or anticlockwise?

    ................................................
    *[1]*

10. A current-carrying conductor in a magnetic field experiences a force. Explain how a loudspeaker makes use of this effect to convert a.c. electrical signals into sound.

    .........................................................................................................................

    .........................................................................................................................

    .........................................................................................................................

    .........................................................................................................................

    .........................................................................................................................
    *[3]*

11. The voltage across a transformer increases from 230 V on the primary coil to 450 000 V on the secondary coil. If the current in the secondary coil is 0.018 A, what is the current in the primary coil? Assume the transformer is 100% efficient.

    .........................................................................................................................

    .........................................................................................................................

    .........................................................................................................................

    .........................................................................................................................

                                        Current = ............................ A
                                                              *[3]*

Paper 2

15

Section 6 — Magnetism and Electromagnetism

# Test 18

There are **11 questions** in this test. Give yourself **10 minutes** to answer them all.

1. True or False? "Magnetic field lines are always drawn pointing from the south pole to the north pole."

   **A**  True

   **B**  False

   *[1]*

2. What is a magnetic material that loses its induced magnetism quickly described as?

   **A**  Magnetically hard

   **B**  Magnetically soft

   **C**  Magnetically uniform

   *[1]*

3. How can a uniform magnetic field pattern be created using two permanent magnets?

   **A**  By placing the north pole of one magnet near the south pole of the other.

   **B**  By placing the two north poles of the magnets near each other.

   **C**  By placing the two south poles of the magnets near each other.

   *[1]*

4. A motor consists of a spinning coil of wire in a magnetic field. To keep the coil spinning, you need to...

   **A**  ... increase the current every half turn.

   **B**  ... increase the magnetic field strength every half turn.

   **C**  ... swap the contacts every half turn.

   *[1]*

5. In a step-up transformer, the secondary coil has...

   **A**  ... fewer turns than the primary coil.

   **B**  ... the same number of turns as the primary coil.

   **C**  ... more turns than the primary coil.

   *[1]*

6. True or False? "Changing the strength of the magnetic field around a stationary electrical conductor will induce a voltage in the conductor."

   **A**  True

   **B**  False

   *[1]*

7. A current-carrying conductor is at 90° to a magnetic field. Which of the following will cause a change in the direction of the force acting on it?

   **A**  Reversing the current through the conductor.

   **B**  Increasing the length of the conductor.

   **C**  Reducing the magnetic field's strength.

   *[1]*

8. The magnetic field lines around a solenoid should be drawn...

   **A**  ... further apart along the centre of the solenoid than outside the solenoid.

   **B**  ... closer together along the centre of the solenoid than outside the solenoid.

   **C**  ... equally close together along the centre and around the outside of the solenoid.

   *[1]*

Paper 2

Paper 2

Section 6 — Magnetism and Electromagnetism

**9.** A flat circular coil of wire is shown below. Draw the magnetic field pattern of the coil on the diagram, including arrows to show the direction of the field.

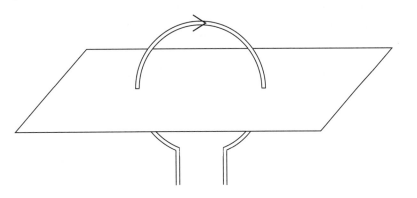

*[2]*

**10.** The diagram shows the force on a current-carrying wire in a magnetic field.

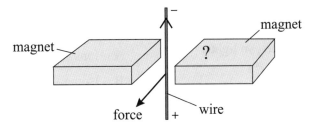

Does the '?' in the diagram mark the north (N) or south (S) pole of the magnet? ............

Justify your answer.

...........................................................................................................................................

...........................................................................................................................................

*[2]*

**11.** Electricity can be generated by rotating a magnet within
a coil of wire to induce a voltage in the coil.
State three ways in which the size of the voltage induced can be increased.

1. ..................................................................................................................................

2. ..................................................................................................................................

3. ..................................................................................................................................

*[3]*

**15**

# Section 7 — Radioactivity and Particles

## Test 19

There are **12 questions** in this test. Give yourself **10 minutes** to answer them all.

1. What happens to a nucleus when it emits a gamma ray?

   **A** Its mass decreases

   **B** Its charge decreases

   **C** Its mass and charge remain unchanged
   *[1]*

2. An object has been irradiated if...

   **A** ... it has been exposed to a radioactive source.

   **B** ... unwanted radioactive atoms have got on to or into it.

   **C** ... it has become radioactive.
   *[1]*

3. What happens in nuclear fusion?

   **A** One heavy nucleus emits a beta particle.

   **B** One heavy nucleus splits into two lighter nuclei.

   **C** Two light nuclei combine to form a heavier nucleus.
   *[1]*

4. What is the name for atoms with the same number of protons but different numbers of neutrons?

   **A** Ions

   **B** Isomers

   **C** Isotopes
   *[1]*

5. What is the role of the shielding around a nuclear reactor?

   **A** To absorb the ionising radiation released during fission.

   **B** To prevent background radiation from entering the reactor.

   **C** To keep the reactor cool.
   *[1]*

6. What are the fission products of a uranium-235 nucleus?

   **A** One radioactive daughter nuclei and a large number of neutrons.

   **B** Two radioactive daughter nuclei and a small number of neutrons.

   **C** Two radioactive daughter nuclei only.
   *[1]*

7. Which type of radiation can penetrate the furthest into materials?

   **A** Alpha

   **B** Beta

   **C** Gamma
   *[1]*

8. Nuclear fusion does not happen at low temperatures and pressures, due to electrostatic repulsion of...

   **A** ... electrons.

   **B** ... protons.

   **C** ... neutrons.
   *[1]*

**9.** Give one source of background radiation.

...................................................................................................................................................
[1]

**10.** Describe two dangers to living organisms of being exposed to ionising radiation.

1. ...........................................................................................................................................

...........................................................................................................................................

2. ...........................................................................................................................................

...........................................................................................................................................
[2]

**11.** The equation below shows the alpha decay of an isotope of americium. Complete the equation by writing the missing atomic number and mass number of the product.

$$^{241}_{95}\text{Am} \rightarrow \,^{.........}_{.........}\text{Np} + \,^{4}_{2}\text{He}$$

[2]

**12.** Use this graph to work out the half-life of the radioactive sample.

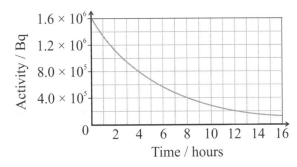

Half-life = .................................... hours
[2]

15

# Test 20

There are **11 questions** in this test. Give yourself **10 minutes** to answer them all.

---

1. Which of the following is the correct symbol for a carbon-14 nucleus?

   **A**  $^{6}_{14}C$

   **B**  $^{14}_{6}C$

   **C**  $^{8}_{6}C$

   *[1]*

2. True or False? "Radioactive waste from nuclear power stations is often difficult to dispose of safely because it has a long half-life."

   **A**  True

   **B**  False

   *[1]*

3. True or False? "When a radioactive nucleus emits a beta particle, its atomic number increases."

   **A**  True

   **B**  False

   *[1]*

4. Which of the following gives the number of neutrons in the nucleus of an atom?

   **A**  The mass number

   **B**  The mass number + the atomic number

   **C**  The mass number – the atomic number

   *[1]*

5. In a nuclear reactor, a uranium-235 nucleus can split when...

   **A**  ... it absorbs gamma radiation.

   **B**  ... it collides with an electron.

   **C**  ... it collides with a neutron.

   *[1]*

6. The count rate of a radioactive sample falls from 130 Bq to 65 Bq in 15 minutes. What is its half-life?

   **A**  15 minutes

   **B**  30 minutes

   **C**  1 hour

   *[1]*

7. Energy is released in a fusion reaction because...

   **A**  ... there is a gain in mass by the nuclei involved in the reaction.

   **B**  ... there is a loss of mass from the nuclei involved in the reaction.

   **C**  ... protons are turned into neutrons during the reaction.

   *[1]*

8. Nuclear fission reactions release high-energy neutrons. The role of the moderator in a nuclear reactor is to...

   **A**  ... limit the rate of fission by absorbing excess neutrons.

   **B**  ... slow the neutrons down so they can be absorbed by uranium nuclei.

   **C**  ... transfer energy from the neutrons to the water in the heat exchanger.

   *[1]*

---

9. The decay of phosphorus-32 is shown below.

$$_{15}^{32}\text{P} \rightarrow \ _{.........}^{32}\text{S} + _{-1}^{0}\text{e}$$

Complete the equation by writing in the missing atomic number of the product.

*[1]*

10. A student has a source of radiation that emits either alpha, beta or gamma radiation. She places the source opposite a Geiger-Muller tube and detector and records the count rate. She then places a sheet of paper between the source and the detector and records the count rate, and then repeats this with a sheet of aluminium instead of paper. Describe how her results will allow her to work out which type of radiation is emitted by the source.

.................................................................................................................................

.................................................................................................................................

.................................................................................................................................

.................................................................................................................................

.................................................................................................................................

*[3]*

11. Nuclear reactors are powered by a controlled chain reaction. Describe how nuclear fission can cause a chain reaction.

.................................................................................................................................

.................................................................................................................................

.................................................................................................................................

.................................................................................................................................

.................................................................................................................................

*[3]*

15

# Section 8 — Astrophysics

# Test 21

There are **10 questions** in this test.  Give yourself **10 minutes** to answer them all.

1.  The Milky Way is...

    **A**  ... the name of our Solar System.

    **B**  ... the name of the galaxy our Solar System is in.

    **C**  ... a collection of billions of galaxies.

    *[1]*

2.  What force allows planets and satellites to maintain their orbits?

    **A**  Magnetic

    **B**  Electrostatic

    **C**  Gravitational

    *[1]*

3.  The Sun is a yellow star.  Which of the following stars will have a lower surface temperature than the Sun?

    **A**  A blue star

    **B**  A white star

    **C**  A red star

    *[1]*

4.  Which of the following statements about a comet's orbit is true?

    **A**  The speed of the comet changes during its orbit.

    **B**  The orbit is slightly elliptical.

    **C**  The Sun is at the centre of the orbit.

    *[1]*

5.  True or False?  "The life cycle of a star depends on its mass."

    **A**  True

    **B**  False

    *[1]*

6.  Which of the following units is gravitational field strength measured in?

    **A**  $N/m^2$

    **B**  N/kg

    **C**  m/s

    *[1]*

7.  True or False?  "The gravitational field strength on the Moon's surface is the same as the gravitational field strength on the Earth's surface."

    **A**  True

    **B**  False

    *[1]*

Paper 2

8.  The absolute magnitude of a star is...

    **A**  ... how bright the star would appear if it was at a standard distance from Earth.

    **B**  ... the brightest the star could appear to an observer.

    **C**  ... how bright the star appears from Earth.

    *[1]*

---

9.  The diagram shows a communications satellite in a circular orbit around the Earth.

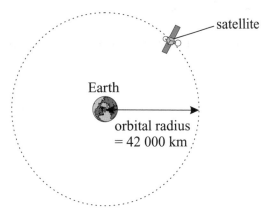

satellite

Earth

orbital radius
= 42 000 km

The satellite has an orbital speed of 3050 m/s. The radius of the satellite's orbit is
42 000 km. Calculate the time taken for the satellite to orbit the Earth once.
Give your answer to two significant figures.

$$\text{orbital speed} = \frac{2 \times \pi \times \text{orbital radius}}{\text{time period}}$$

.........................................................................................................................

.........................................................................................................................

.........................................................................................................................

Time taken = ............................................... s

*[3]*

10. Explain how red-shift provides evidence that the universe is expanding.

.........................................................................................................................

.........................................................................................................................

.........................................................................................................................

.........................................................................................................................

.........................................................................................................................

.........................................................................................................................

*[4]*

**15**

Section 8 — Astrophysics

Paper 2

# Test 22

There are **11 questions** in this test. Give yourself **10 minutes** to answer them all.

1. What unit is orbital speed measured in?

   **A**   m/s

   **B**   m/s²

   **C**   ms

   *[1]*

2. True or False? "The colour of a star is related to the star's surface temperature."

   **A**   True

   **B**   False

   *[1]*

3. Which of the following objects has the longest orbital time period?

   **A**   Earth

   **B**   The Moon

   **C**   A comet

   *[1]*

4. Which of the following does **not** orbit a planet?

   **A**   a moon

   **B**   a comet

   **C**   an artificial satellite

   *[1]*

5. Which of the following will eventually become a supernova?

   **A**   Stars with a similar mass to the Sun.

   **B**   Stars with a larger mass than the Sun.

   **C**   Stars with a smaller mass than the Sun.

   *[1]*

6. Which of these statements is **incorrect**?

   **A**   The universe contains billions of galaxies.

   **B**   The universe contains billions of stars.

   **C**   The universe is known as the Milky Way.

   *[1]*

7. The gravitational field strength on the surface of the planet Mercury is smaller than the gravitational field strength on the Earth's surface. This is because Mercury has a...

   **A**   ... larger mass than Earth.

   **B**   ... smaller mass than Earth.

   **C**   ... higher surface temperature than Earth.

   *[1]*

8. On a Hertzsprung-Russell diagram, white dwarfs group together because they have...

   **A**   ... negative absolute magnitudes and high temperatures.

   **B**   ... negative absolute magnitudes and low temperatures.

   **C**   ... positive absolute magnitudes and high temperatures.

   *[1]*

Paper 2

**9.** Name stages A and B in the life cycle of the star shown below.

|  |  |  |  |
|---|---|---|---|
| **A** | main sequence star | red giant | **B** |

**A** = ................................................... **B** = ...........................................................

[2]

**10.** In a main sequence star, the outward pressure produced by nuclear fusion balances the force of gravity. What causes this phase in the star's life cycle to end?

.............................................................................................................................................

.............................................................................................................................................

[1]

**11.** Galaxy X travels at a speed of $4.5 \times 10^7$ m/s away from Earth. The difference in wavelength between the light emitted by the galaxy and the observed wavelength is 72 nm. Calculate the wavelength of the light emitted by the galaxy.

The speed of light is $3.00 \times 10^8$ m/s.

$$\frac{\text{change in wavelength}}{\text{reference wavelength}} = \frac{\text{velocity of a galaxy}}{\text{speed of light}}$$

.............................................................................................................................................

.............................................................................................................................................

.............................................................................................................................................

.............................................................................................................................................

Wavelength = ................................................ m

[4]

| 15 |

Paper 2

Section 8 — Astrophysics

# Test 23

There are **10 questions** in this test. Give yourself **10 minutes** to answer them all.

**1.** If the resultant force on a moving object is zero, the object will...

   **A**  ... slow down and eventually stop.

   **B**  ... keep moving at a steady speed.

*[1]*

**2.** True or False? "Gamma rays are more strongly ionising than alpha particles."

   **A**  True

   **B**  False

*[1]*

**3.** Which type of current is supplied by a battery?

   **A**  Alternating current (ac)

   **B**  Direct current (dc)

   **C**  Cell current (cc)

*[1]*

**4.** Which of the following is not formed after a supernova?

   **A**  A neutron star

   **B**  A black hole

   **C**  A red supergiant

*[1]*

**5.** Why does increasing the volume in which a gas is contained at a constant temperature cause the pressure to decrease?

   **A**  The particles hit the walls of the container with less force.

   **B**  The particles hit the walls of the container less often.

   **C**  The particles hit the walls of the container at a slower speed.

*[1]*

**6.** An X-ray travels at $3.0 \times 10^8$ m/s and has a frequency of $3 \times 10^{17}$ Hz. What is the wavelength of the X-ray?

   **A**  $1 \times 10^{-9}$ m

   **B**  $1 \times 10^{25}$ m

   **C**  $1 \times 10^{9}$ m

*[1]*

**7.** A cannon uses explosives to launch a ball into the air. Which is an unwanted energy transfer that occurs when the cannon is fired?

   **A**  Chemical energy store of explosives → Kinetic energy store of ball

   **B**  Chemical energy store of explosives → Gravitational potential energy store of ball

   **C**  Chemical energy store of explosives → Thermal energy store of ball

*[1]*

**8.** In which of the following situations will a voltage **not** be induced in the conductor?

   **A**  The strength of the magnetic field passing through the conductor is decreasing.

   **B**  The magnetic field passing through the stationary conductor is steady.

   **C**  The conductor is moving with a constant speed through a steady magnetic field.

*[1]*

**9.** The graph on the right shows the motion of a lorry.

Use the graph to calculate the acceleration of the lorry between 4 s and 11 s. Give your answer to two significant figures.

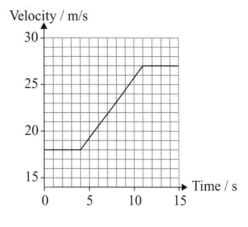

Velocity / m/s

Time / s

.......................................................................................................

.......................................................................................................

.......................................................................................................

.......................................................................................................

Acceleration = ........................... m/s$^2$

*[4]*

**10.** A circuit diagram is shown on the right. Calculate the current passing through the circuit when component X has a resistance of 3.0 Ω.

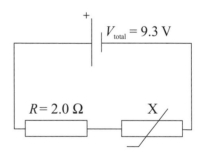

$V_{total} = 9.3$ V

$R = 2.0$ Ω        X

.......................................................................................................

.......................................................................................................

.......................................................................................................

Current = ........................... A

*[3]*

15

# Test 24

There are **10 questions** in this test.  Give yourself **10 minutes** to answer them all.

1.  A speaker is connected to a 2 V battery. How much energy is transferred to the speaker when 80 C of charge passes through it?

    **A**   40 J

    **B**   82 J

    **C**   160 J

    *[1]*

2.  A ray passes from air into glass which has a refractive index of 1.5.  The angle of refraction is 35°.  If the angle of incidence is *i*, which of the following is true?

    **A**   $\sin i \approx 0.38$

    **B**   $\sin i \approx 0.86$

    **C**   $\sin i \approx 2.6$

    *[1]*

3.  A ship has an average speed of 2.5 m/s. How long will it take it to move 2.4 km?

    **A**   16 minutes

    **B**   20 minutes

    **C**   8 minutes

    *[1]*

4.  What is 100 K in degrees Celsius?

    **A**   373 °C

    **B**   27 °C

    **C**   −173 °C

    *[1]*

5.  A ball travels at 6 m/s.  It has 4.5 J of energy in its kinetic energy store.  What is the mass of the ball?

    **A**   0.13 kg

    **B**   0.25 kg

    **C**   1.5 kg

    *[1]*

6.  In the left-hand rule, the directions of which variables are represented by your thumb and first two fingers?

    **A**   Motion, current and magnetic field

    **B**   Current and magnetic field only

    **C**   Current, magnetic field and induced voltage

    *[1]*

7.  What is the unit of activity of a radioactive isotope?

    **A**   Joule, J

    **B**   Hertz, Hz

    **C**   Becquerel, Bq

    *[1]*

8.  True or False?  "A star that emits blue light will have a higher surface temperature than a star that emits red light."

    **A**   True

    **B**   False

    *[1]*

9.  The graph on the right shows the number of radioactive nuclei in an archaeological sample over time.
    Use the graph to calculate the half-life of the radioactive sample and calculate the number of radioactive nuclei left in the sample after $16.8 \times 10^3$ years.

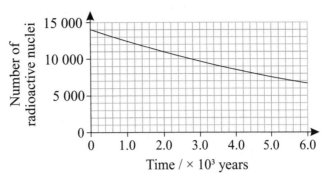

.................................................................................................................................

.................................................................................................................................

.................................................................................................................................

.................................................................................................................................

Half-life = ........................... years

Number of nuclei = .......................................

[4]

10. An electric pencil sharpener has an efficiency of 75%. Calculate the useful energy output of the pencil sharpener, given it has a total energy output of 560 J.

.................................................................................................................................

.................................................................................................................................

.................................................................................................................................

Energy = .............................................. J

[3]

15

# Test 25

There are **11 questions** in this test.  Give yourself **10 minutes** to answer them all.

1.  A current of 0.21 A flows through a resistor for 3 s.  How much charge has passed through the resistor?

    **A**   0.07 C

    **B**   0.63 C

    **C**   1.89 C

    *[1]*

2.  A driving force of 400 N acts on a car of mass 1500 kg.  The car experiences frictional forces of 100 N.
    What is the car's acceleration?

    **A**   0.20 m/s²

    **B**   5 m/s²

    **C**   0.33 m/s²

    *[1]*

3.  Which of these is a use of gamma radiation?

    **A**   Cooking food

    **B**   Communications

    **C**   Sterilising food

    *[1]*

4.  An object is absorbing radiation at a faster rate than it is emitting radiation.  What is happening to its temperature?

    **A**   It is decreasing

    **B**   It is remaining constant

    **C**   It is increasing

    *[1]*

5.  A sealed container of gas has a pressure of $3.0 \times 10^5$ Pa.  Each side of the container has an area of 0.040 m².  What force does the gas exert on each side?

    **A**   $1.3 \times 10^{-7}$ N

    **B**   $1.2 \times 10^4$ N

    **C**   $7.5 \times 10^6$ N

    *[1]*

6.  A voltage is induced in a coil of wire by rotating it in a magnetic field.  Which of the following changes would increase the voltage induced?

    **A**   Reducing the speed of rotation

    **B**   Increasing the strength of magnetic field

    **C**   Reducing the number turns of the coil

    *[1]*

7.  Which type of radiation is the same as a helium nucleus?

    **A**   Alpha

    **B**   Beta

    **C**   Gamma

    *[1]*

8.  The force between the north poles of two bar magnets is...

    **A**   ... attractive.

    **B**   ... repulsive.

    *[1]*

**9.** An observer measures the frequency of a passing ambulance's siren with an oscilloscope. After the ambulance passes the observer, a decrease in the siren's frequency is recorded. Name the effect that causes this change in frequency and explain why it happens.

Name of the effect: ..................................................................................................

Explanation: ..........................................................................................................

...............................................................................................................................

...............................................................................................................................

[2]

**10.** In a toaster, an electrical current flows through a coil with a high resistance. Describe how this causes the bread to be heated.

...............................................................................................................................

...............................................................................................................................

...............................................................................................................................

[2]

**11.** A velocity-time graph for a racing car is shown on the right.

Calculate the distance travelled by the car in the first 15 s of its journey.

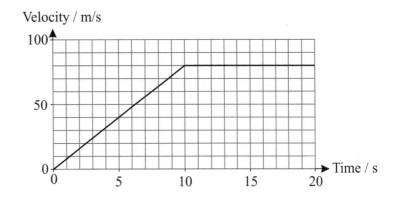

...............................................................................................................................

...............................................................................................................................

...............................................................................................................................

Distance = ...................... m

[3]

15

# Test 26

There are **10 questions** in this test. Give yourself **10 minutes** to answer them all.

1. A 70 g hailstone is falling at its terminal velocity. Given $g = 10$ N/kg, what is the upward force acting on the hailstone?

   **A** 7 N

   **B** 0 N

   **C** 0.7 N

   [1]

2. What happens to the resistance of an LDR as the intensity of light shone on it increases?

   **A** It does not change

   **B** It increases

   **C** It decreases

   [1]

3. Which of the following lists is in order of increasing wavelength?

   **A** Red, green, violet

   **B** Green, violet, red

   **C** Violet, green, red

   [1]

4. Which energy store is energy usefully transferred to in a blender?

   **A** The kinetic energy store of the blades

   **B** The elastic potential energy store of the blades

   **C** The gravitational potential energy store of the blades

   [1]

5. Electric heater A has a power of 1 kW. Electric heater B has a power of 880 W. Which transfers the most energy in 2 hours?

   **A** Heater A

   **B** Heater B

   [1]

6. True or False? "The pressure of a gas held at constant volume decreases if the temperature is decreased."

   **A** True

   **B** False

   [1]

7. A bicycle's brakes exert a force of 1400 N, bringing the bicycle to a complete stop in 3.5 m. What is the work done by the brakes?

   **A** 4900 J

   **B** 1400 J

   **C** 400 J

   [1]

8. Which process releases energy in stars?

   **A** Combustion

   **B** Nuclear fission

   **C** Nuclear fusion

   [1]

**9.** The circuit diagram below shows two resistors
connected in series with a battery.

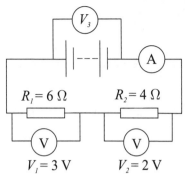

Find the reading on voltmeter $V_3$.

...................................................................................................................................

Voltage = ............ V

Find the total resistance, $R$, of the circuit.

...................................................................................................................................

Resistance = ............ Ω

Find the reading on the ammeter.

...................................................................................................................................

...................................................................................................................................

Current = ............... A

*[4]*

**10.** A car accelerates at 2.50 m/s² over a distance of 14.0 m. Its final speed is 13.6 m/s.
What was the initial speed of the car?

(final speed)² = (initial speed)² + (2 × acceleration × distance moved)

...................................................................................................................................

...................................................................................................................................

...................................................................................................................................

Initial speed = .................. m/s

*[3]*

15

# Test 27

There are **11 questions** in this test. Give yourself **10 minutes** to answer them all.

**1.** An electromagnet is usually made from...

**A** ... a straight, current-carrying wire.

**B** ... a current-carrying coil of wire.

**C** ... a block of magnetic material.

*[1]*

**2.** Which of the following is an electrical conductor?

**A** Silver

**B** Plastic

**C** Rubber

*[1]*

**3.** If unwanted radioactive atoms get onto or into an object, the object has been...

**A** ... irradiated.

**B** ... sterilised.

**C** ... contaminated.

*[1]*

**4.** An 800 W microwave oven is supplied by a 230 V mains voltage. What is the rating of the fuse needed?

**A** 3 A

**B** 5 A

**C** 13 A

*[1]*

**5.** In general, the further away a galaxy is...

**A** ... the smaller the observed increase in the wavelength of its light.

**B** ... the slower it is moving away from us.

**C** ... the bigger the observed increase in wavelength of its light.

*[1]*

**6.** Which of the following is **not** evidence that supports the Big Bang theory?

**A** Variation in gravitational field strength.

**B** The red-shift observed in light reaching Earth from distant galaxies

**C** Cosmic microwave background radiation

*[1]*

**7.** Which of the following is a way that seat belts reduce the risk of injury to wearers.

**A** They slow down the wearer more quickly.

**B** They reduce the total change in momentum of the wearer.

**C** They reduce the rate of change of momentum of the wearer.

*[1]*

**8.** Object A is travelling to the left and collides with the stationary object B. After the collision, object B moves away to the left. Which of the following is true of object A's momentum after the collision?

**A** It is the same as it was before the collision.

**B** It is lower than it was before the collision.

**C** It is higher than it was before the collision.

*[1]*

9. On this oscilloscope trace of a sound wave, the timebase is set to 0.005 s/div.

Calculate the frequency of the wave shown.

$$\text{period} = \frac{1}{\text{frequency}}$$

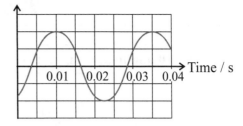

..............................................................................................................................

..............................................................................................................................

..............................................................................................................................

Frequency = ......................... Hz

[3]

10. Complete the Hertzsprung-Russell diagram on the right to show the area of the graph in which white dwarfs are found and the area of the graph in which red giants and supergiants are found.

Label the white dwarfs with a W and the red giants and supergiants with an R.

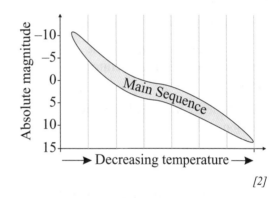

[2]

11. A student uses a heater to provide energy to three 0.5 kg blocks made from different materials. The student supplies the same amount of energy to each block. She measures their temperatures at regular intervals for five minutes. The graph on the right shows her results. State and explain which block of material has the highest specific heat capacity.

..............................................................................................................................

..............................................................................................................................

..............................................................................................................................

[2]

15

# Test 28

There are **10 questions** in this test. Give yourself **10 minutes** to answer them all.

1. A teapot is stationary on a table. The teapot exerts a force of 10 N on the table. What is the reaction force applied to the teapot by the table?

   **A**   0 N

   **B**   −10 N

   **C**   − 20 N

   *[1]*

2. A car with a mass of 1500 kg is travelling at a velocity of 10 m/s when it has to stop suddenly. What is the decrease in the car's momentum?

   **A**   15 000 kg m/s

   **B**   1500 kg m/s

   **C**   150 kg m/s

   *[1]*

3. What is cosmic microwave background (CMB) radiation believed to be?

   **A**   Energy from exploding supernovae.

   **B**   Radiation given out by man-made objects in space, such as satellites and telescopes.

   **C**   Leftover energy from the Big Bang explosion.

   *[1]*

4. Which of these is an environmental problem caused by generating electricity using hydroelectric power?

   **A**   It could result in a loss of habitat for some species.

   **B**   It results in the release of sulfur dioxide, which causes acid rain.

   **C**   The waste produced is dangerous and difficult to get rid of.

   *[1]*

5. Which of the following correctly shows the relationship between voltage, $V$, current, $I$, and resistance, $R$?

   **A**   $V = I \times R$

   **B**   $V = I \div R$

   **C**   $V = I \times R^2$

   *[1]*

6. The amount of energy needed to raise the temperature of 1 kg of a substance by 1 °C is...

   **A**   ... its boiling point.

   **B**   ... its specific heat capacity.

   **C**   ... its change in heat capacity.

   *[1]*

7. What is the name of the process by which light travels along an optical fibre?

   **A**   Total internal refraction

   **B**   Total external reflection

   **C**   Total internal reflection

   *[1]*

8. Absolute magnitude is a measure of how bright a given star would appear to be if it were...

   **A**   ... a fixed size.

   **B**   ... a fixed distance from Earth.

   **C**   ... a fixed temperature.

   *[1]*

**9.** The voltage across the primary coil of a transformer is 54.0 V and the voltage across the secondary coil is 32.0 V. The current in the primary coil is a 8.00 A. Calculate the current in the secondary coil. Assume the transformer is 100% efficient.

................................................................................................................................

................................................................................................................................

................................................................................................................................

Current in secondary coil = ............................. A

[3]

**10.** The diagram below shows a 10 m long beam suspended by two cables (A and B) at its ends. A 560 N weight is placed on the beam, 2.5 m from one end. Ignore the effect of the weight of the beam.

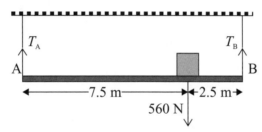

Calculate the tension in cable A, $T_A$, and the tension in cable B, $T_B$.

................................................................................................................................

................................................................................................................................

................................................................................................................................

................................................................................................................................

$T_A$ = .................................... N

$T_B$ = .................................... N

[4]

15

# Test 29

PAPER 2

There are **10 questions** in this test. Give yourself **10 minutes** to answer them all.

1. What is the name of the point through which the weight of an object acts?

   A   The centre of gravity

   B   The centre of weight

   C   The centre of contact

   *[1]*

2. Photocopiers make use of electrostatic charges. Negatively charged toner powder is attracted to areas of the paper that...

   A   ... are positively charged.

   B   ... are negatively charged.

   C   ... have excess electrons.

   *[1]*

3. Avoiding strong sunlight reduces the risks to the human body from...

   A   ... gamma rays.

   B   ... microwaves.

   C   ... ultraviolet.

   *[1]*

4. Kettle A takes 160 s to boil a litre of water. Kettle B takes 210 s to boil a litre of water. Both kettles have the same efficiency. Which kettle has the highest power?

   A   Kettle A

   B   Kettle B

   *[1]*

5. What are the units for specific heat capacity?

   A   kg/J °C

   B   J/kg °C

   C   °C/Jkg

   *[1]*

6. A transformer has twice as many turns on its secondary coil as on its primary coil. The voltage across the primary coil is 10 V. What is the voltage across the secondary coil?

   A   5 V

   B   10 V

   C   20 V

   *[1]*

7. Light from galaxies is red-shifted. What do measurements of the red-shift tell us?

   A   All galaxies are moving away from us at the same speed.

   B   More distant galaxies are moving away faster than closer galaxies.

   C   Closer galaxies are moving away faster than distant galaxies.

   *[1]*

8. How can a change of state be identified on a temperature-time graph?

   A   The graph is horizontal during a change of state.

   B   The gradient of the graph increases during a change of state.

   C   The gradient of the graph decreases during a change of state.

   *[1]*

---

Mixed Tests for Paper 2

**9.** The image below shows the national grid.

State the name given to the electrical devices labelled X, and describe their purpose in the national grid.

.................................................................................................................................

.................................................................................................................................

.................................................................................................................................

.................................................................................................................................

.................................................................................................................................

*[3]*

**10.** The diagram below shows a gun being fired. The gun is initially stationary, then moves backwards when it is fired.

Use the principle of conservation of momentum to find the recoil speed of the gun.

.................................................................................................................................

.................................................................................................................................

.................................................................................................................................

.................................................................................................................................

Speed = ........................... m/s

*[4]*

15

---

# Test 30

There are **11 questions** in this test. Give yourself **10 minutes** to answer them all.

1. The total momentum after a collision is...

   **A** ... the same as the total momentum before the collision.

   **B** ... always zero.

   **C** ... greater than the total momentum before the collision.

   *[1]*

2. What is the moment of a 30 N force acting on a lever at a perpendicular distance of 0.15 m from the pivot?

   **A** 4.5 Nm

   **B** 60 Nm

   **C** 200 Nm

   *[1]*

3. An electric kettle is supplied with 750 000 J of energy from the mains. It usefully transfers 570 000 J of energy to boil the water inside it. What is the efficiency of the kettle?

   **A** 24%

   **B** 76%

   **C** 132%

   *[1]*

4. Electricity is transferred across step-up transformers to...

   **A** ... increase its voltage for transmission from power stations.

   **B** ... increase its current for domestic use.

   **C** ... increase its current for transmission from power stations.

   *[1]*

5. When a charged particle moves in a magnetic field it...

   **A** ... loses its charge.

   **B** ... affects the strength of the magnetic field.

   **C** ... experiences a force.

   *[1]*

6. True or False? "The atomic number of a nucleus will increase by 2 if it emits an alpha particle."

   **A** True

   **B** False

   *[1]*

7. According to the Big Bang theory, when the universe began it was...

   **A** ... small, dense and hot.

   **B** ... identical to the current universe.

   **C** ... much larger and cooler than the current universe.

   *[1]*

8. True or False? "The particles in a gas are further apart than the particles in a solid but are arranged more regularly."

   **A** True

   **B** False

   *[1]*

---

**9.** Describe one disadvantage of generating electricity using nuclear power.

.......................................................................................................................................................

.......................................................................................................................................................

*[1]*

**10.** The diagram on the right shows a light ray being refracted as it enters a glass block.

Calculate the refractive index of the block. Give your answer to two significant figures.

.......................................................................................................................................................

.......................................................................................................................................................

.......................................................................................................................................................

refractive index = ................

*[3]*

**11.** Light from Galaxy A observed on Earth has a wavelength of $6.21 \times 10^{-7}$ m.
When emitted by the galaxy, the light had a wavelength of $5.75 \times 10^{-7}$ m.
Calculate the velocity at which Galaxy A is travelling away from Earth.
The speed of light is $3.00 \times 10^{8}$ m/s.

$$\frac{\text{change in wavelength}}{\text{reference wavelength}} = \frac{\text{velocity of a galaxy}}{\text{speed of light}}$$

.......................................................................................................................................................

.......................................................................................................................................................

.......................................................................................................................................................

Velocity = ........................ m/s

*[3]*

15

# Answers

## Section 1 — Forces and Motion

### Test 1 — Pages 2–3

1. C *[1 mark]*
2. A *[1 mark]*
3. B *[1 mark]*
4. B *[1 mark]*
5. A *[1 mark]*
6. C *[1 mark]*
7. B *[1 mark]*
8. B *[1 mark]*
9. The stopping distance takes into account the driver's thinking distance as well as the vehicle's braking distance *[1 mark]*.
10.

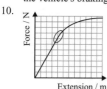

*[1 mark for marking a point on the graph in the region indicated]*
11. average speed = $\dfrac{\text{distance moved}}{\text{time taken}}$
    From the graph, distance moved after
    11 s = 28 m *[1 mark]*
    So average speed = 28 ÷ 11
    = 2.545... m/s
    (or 2.5 m/s to 2 s.f.)
    *[1 mark]*
12. $F = \dfrac{mv - mu}{t}$
    $= \dfrac{(90 \times 3.2) - (90 \times 5.8)}{7}$
    *[1 mark]*
    = −33.428... *[1 mark]*
    = −33 N (to 2 s.f.) *[1 mark]*

### Test 2 — Pages 4–5

1. C *[1 mark]*
2. C *[1 mark]*
3. A *[1 mark]*
4. A *[1 mark]*
5. B *[1 mark]*
6. A *[1 mark]*
7. B *[1 mark]*
8. A *[1 mark]*
9. Between A and B, the object has a constant acceleration *[1 mark]*. Between B and C the object's acceleration gradually decreases *[1 mark]*. Between C and D the object has an acceleration of 0 m/s² *[1 mark]*.
10. total momentum before collision = total momentum after collision
    So total momentum after collision
    = 3.2 + 0 = 3.2 kg m/s *[1 mark]*
    total mass after collision
    = 0.70 + 0.080 = 0.78 kg
    Rearrange the formula:
    velocity = momentum ÷ mass *[1 mark]*
    velocity = 3.2 ÷ 0.78 *[1 mark]*
    = 4.102... m/s
    (or 4.1 m/s to 2 s.f.) *[1 mark]*

### Test 3 — Pages 6–7

1. B *[1 mark]*
2. C *[1 mark]*
3. B *[1 mark]*
4. C *[1 mark]*
5. A *[1 mark]*
6. C *[1 mark]*
7. A *[1 mark]*
8. B *[1 mark]*
9. $W = m \times g$
    $= 83 \times 10$
    = 830 N *[1 mark]*
10. Resultant horizontal force
    = 78 N + 52 N −130 N = 0 N *[1 mark]*
    Resultant vertical force
    = 91 N − 52 N − 39 N = 0 N *[1 mark]*
    Resultant force = 0 N *[1 mark]*
11. (final speed)² = (initial speed)² + (2 × acceleration × distance moved)
    or $v^2 = u^2 + (2 \times a \times s)$
    Rearrange for $a$:
    $a = \dfrac{v^2 - u^2}{2s}$ *[1 mark]*
    $= \dfrac{0^2 - 13^2}{2 \times 26}$ *[1 mark]*
    = −3.25 m/s²
    deceleration = 3.25 m/s²
    = 3.3 m/s² (to 2 s.f.) *[1 mark]*

### Test 4 — Pages 8–9

1. C *[1 mark]*
2. A *[1 mark]*
3. B *[1 mark]*
4. C *[1 mark]*
5. B *[1 mark]*
6. B *[1 mark]*
7. A *[1 mark]*
8. B *[1 mark]*
9. The object initially accelerates due to gravity *[1 mark]*. As the object's speed increases, the frictional forces on the object increase, until they match the force due to gravity and the resultant force on the object is zero *[1 mark]*. And so the object moves at terminal velocity (steady speed) *[1 mark]*.
10. The rod's weight acts at its centre, so the perpendicular distance of the weight from the pivot is 8.0 ÷ 2 = 4.0 m *[1 mark]*.
    moment of a force = force × perpendicular distance from the pivot
    So the clockwise moment is
    4.0 × 1500 = 6000 Nm *[1 mark]*
    The rod is at rest so anticlockwise moment = clockwise moment *[1 mark]*
    To find the force on the rope, rearrange the formula for force:
    force = moment ÷ distance
    = 6000 ÷ 8.0 = 750 N *[1 mark]*

## Section 2 — Electricity

### Test 5 — Pages 10–11

1. B *[1 mark]*
2. C *[1 mark]*
3. A *[1 mark]*
4. C *[1 mark]*
5. C *[1 mark]*
6. B *[1 mark]*
7. B *[1 mark]*
8. A *[1 mark]*
9. The fuse melts, which breaks the circuit / stops the current flow *[1 mark]*.
10. Convert energy into J:
    5.4 kJ = 5400 J *[1 mark]*
    energy transferred = charge × voltage
    or $E = Q \times V$
    Rearrange the formula:
    $Q = E \div V$
    = 5400 ÷ 1.2 *[1 mark]*
    = 4500 C *[1 mark]*
11. As more current flows through the lamp, the temperature of the filament increases *[1 mark]*. As the temperature increases, the resistance increases *[1 mark]*. More resistance means that less current can flow for a given voltage and so the graph gets flatter *[1 mark]*.

### Test 6 — Pages 12–13

1. A *[1 mark]*
2. A *[1 mark]*
3. C *[1 mark]*
4. C *[1 mark]*
5. B *[1 mark]*
6. A *[1 mark]*
7. C *[1 mark]*
8. B *[1 mark]*
9. Power = current × voltage
    Or $P = I \times V$ *[1 mark]*
    Rearrange the formula:
    $I = P \div V$
    = 150 ÷ 230 *[1 mark]*
    = 0.652...
    = 0.65 A (to 2 s.f.) *[1 mark]*
10. Because electrons have been transferred to the balloon from the hair *[1 mark]*, the hair has been left with a positive charge *[1 mark]*. The balloon and hair attract one another as they are oppositely charged *[1 mark]*.
11. When the power supply is connected, electrons flow through the copper strip *[1 mark]*.

# Answers

## Test 7 — Pages 14–15

1. B *[1 mark]*  2. B *[1 mark]*
3. B *[1 mark]*  4. C *[1 mark]*
5. B *[1 mark]*  6. C *[1 mark]*
7. A *[1 mark]*  8. C *[1 mark]*
9. Voltage = current × resistance
   Or $V = I \times R$
   Rearrange the formula:
   $I = V \div R$
   $= 16 \div 40$ *[1 mark]*
   $= 0.4$ A *[1 mark]*
10. When a current flows through a resistor, the electrons collide with the ions in the lattice that make up the resistor *[1 mark]*. This transfers energy to the ions, causing them to vibrate more and the resistor to heat up *[1 mark]*.
11. Energy transferred = current × voltage × time
    or $E = I \times V \times t$
    Rearrange the formula:
    $t = E \div (I \times V)$ *[1 mark]*
    $= 1\,062\,600 \div (11 \times 230)$ *[1 mark]*
    $= 420$ s *[1 mark]*

## Section 3 — Waves

### Test 8 — Pages 16-17

1. C *[1 mark]*  2. B *[1 mark]*
3. A *[1 mark]*  4. A *[1 mark]*
5. B *[1 mark]*  6. C *[1 mark]*
7. C *[1 mark]*  8. B *[1 mark]*
9. A: microwaves *[1 mark]*
   D: X-rays *[1 mark]*
10. Any two from: e.g. in night vision equipment, in heating/to keep people warm, in cooking *[1 mark for each]*.
11. Place both microphones next to the speaker, then slowly move one away until the two detected waves on the oscilloscope display are aligned, but have moved exactly one wavelength apart *[1 mark]*. Measure the distance between the two microphones to find one wavelength, λ *[1 mark]*. Use the formula $v = f\lambda$, where $f$ is the frequency of the signal generator and so the sound waves, to find the velocity of the sound waves, $v$, passing through the air *[1 mark]*.

## Test 9 — Pages 18–19

1. C *[1 mark]*  2. B *[1 mark]*
3. B *[1 mark]*  4. A *[1 mark]*
5. A *[1 mark]*  6. C *[1 mark]*
7. A *[1 mark]*  8. B *[1 mark]*
9. E.g.

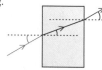

*[1 mark for showing the ray bending towards the normal as it passes into the block and then travelling in a straight line until it reaches the other side of the block, 1 mark for showing the ray bending away from the normal as it exits the block, parallel to the original incident ray]*

10. wave speed = frequency × wavelength *[1 mark]*
    $= 3.0 \times 10^7 \times 1.4$ *[1 mark]*
    $= 4.2 \times 10^7$ m/s
    (or 42 000 000 m/s) *[1 mark]*
11. Similarity: Same pitch *[1 mark]*
    Difference: A is louder than B *[1 mark]*

## Test 10 — Pages 20-21

1. B *[1 mark]*  2. A *[1 mark]*
3. B *[1 mark]*  4. A *[1 mark]*
5. C *[1 mark]*  6. B *[1 mark]*
7. B *[1 mark]*  8. A *[1 mark]*
9. Any two from: e.g. microwaves — internal heating of body tissues / infrared — skin burns / ultraviolet — damage to surface cells/blindness/skin cancer / gamma rays — mutation or damage to cells in the body/cancer *[1 mark for each]*
10. Rearrange for time period:
    time period = 1 ÷ frequency
    $= 1 \div 4$ *[1 mark]*
    $= 0.25$ s *[1 mark]*
11. Refractive index = sin $i$ ÷ sin $r$
    $= \sin 40° \div \sin 26°$ *[1 mark]*
    $= 1.4663...$ *[1 mark]*
    $= 1.5$ (to 2 s.f.) *[1 mark]*

## Section 4 — Energy Resources and Energy Transfer

### Test 11 — Pages 22-23

1. B *[1 mark]*  2. A *[1 mark]*
3. C *[1 mark]*  4. C *[1 mark]*
5. B *[1 mark]*  6. A *[1 mark]*
7. A *[1 mark]*  8. B *[1 mark]*
9. E.g. they can alter the landscape/spoil the view. They can alter the local habitat for wildlife *[1 mark for each correct answer]*.
10. $KE = \frac{1}{2} \times m \times v^2$
    $= \frac{1}{2} \times 580 \times 65^2$ *[1 mark]*
    $= 1\,225\,250$ J
    (or 1 200 000 J to 2 s.f.) *[1 mark]*
11. work done to bring a vehicle to rest = the vehicle's initial kinetic energy
    or $F \times d = KE$ *[1 mark]*
    Rearrange for $d$:
    $d = KE \div F$
    $= 1\,417\,500 \div 56\,000$ *[1 mark]*
    $= 25.3125$ m (or 25 m to 2 s.f.) *[1 mark]*

### Test 12 — Pages 24-25

1. B *[1 mark]*  2. C *[1 mark]*
3. C *[1 mark]*  4. B *[1 mark]*
5. B *[1 mark]*  6. B *[1 mark]*
7. A *[1 mark]*  8. A *[1 mark]*
9. 500 g = 0.5 kg
   gravitational potential energy = mass × gravitational field strength × height
   height = gravitational potential energy ÷ (mass × $g$) *[1 mark]*
   $= 100 \div (0.5 \times 10)$ *[1 mark]*
   $= 20$ m *[1 mark]*
10. E.g. fill the Leslie cube with boiling water *[1 mark]*. Hold an infrared detector a set distance away from each of the cube's vertical faces *[1 mark]*, and record the amount of IR radiation it detects from each face *[1 mark]*. To make sure the investigation is fair, after waiting for the cube to warm up, hold a thermometer against both faces to check that they are the same temperature / make sure the infrared detector is placed an identical distance from each side *[1 mark]*.

# Answers

## Test 13 — Pages 26-27

1. A *[1 mark]*  2. A *[1 mark]*
3. C *[1 mark]*  4. B *[1 mark]*
5. A *[1 mark]*  6. A *[1 mark]*
7. C *[1 mark]*  8. B *[1 mark]*
9. The thermal energy store of the hairdryer heater/air. The kinetic energy store of the fan blades/air. *[1 mark for each correct answer]*
10. gravitational potential energy = mass × gravitational field strength × height or $GPE = m \times g \times h$. *[1 mark]*
    So the energy lost from her GPE store is:
    $GPE = 70 \times 10 \times 4000$ *[1 mark]*
    = 2 800 000 J *[1 mark]*
11. The 1200 J of input energy is represented by 20 squares on the Sankey diagram, so 1 square = 1200 ÷ 20 = 60 J.
    The energy usefully transferred is equal to the energy transferred to the motor's kinetic energy store, which is represented by 15 squares. So energy usefully transferred = 15 × 60 = 900 J. *[1 mark]*
    efficiency = $\dfrac{\text{useful energy output}}{\text{total energy output}} \times 100$
    = (900 ÷ 1200) × 100 *[1 mark]*
    = 75% *[1 mark]*

## Test 14 — Pages 28-29

1. B *[1 mark]*  2. C *[1 mark]*
3. A *[1 mark]*  4. C *[1 mark]*
5. A *[1 mark]*  6. B *[1 mark]*
7. B *[1 mark]*  8. C *[1 mark]*
9. Energy is transferred from the Sun to a solar cell by radiation / light *[1 mark]*.
10. 2 mins = 2 × 60 = 120 s
    energy transferred = work done
    power = work done ÷ time taken
    work done = power × time taken
    = 50 × 120 *[1 mark]*
    = 6000 J *[1 mark]*
11. Kinetic energy of the pinball
    = 7.0 − 0.50 = 6.5 J. *[1 mark]*
    Kinetic energy = ½ × mass × speed² or $KE = \frac{1}{2} \times m \times v^2$
    Rearranging this equation for $v$ gives:
    $v = \sqrt{\dfrac{2 \times KE}{m}}$ *[1 mark]*
    $= \sqrt{\dfrac{2 \times 6.5}{0.080}}$ *[1 mark]*
    = 12.74... m/s
    = 13 m/s (to 2 s.f.) *[1 mark]*

## Section 5 — Solids, Liquids and Gases

### Test 15 — Pages 30–31

1. A *[1 mark]*  2. B *[1 mark]*
3. C *[1 mark]*  4. B *[1 mark]*
5. A *[1 mark]*  6. A *[1 mark]*
7. C *[1 mark]*  8. B *[1 mark]*
9. $P_1 \times V_1 = P_2 \times V_2$
   Rearrange for $V_2$:
   $V_2 = (P_1 \times V_1) \div P_2$ *[1 mark]*
   Since this is a ratio, you don't need to change the units into Pa and m³.
   $V_2 = (160 \times 290) \div 110$ *[1 mark]*
   = 421.8... cm³
   = 420 cm³ (to 2 s.f.) *[1 mark]*
10. 4.0 cm = 0.040 m
    So the volume of the cube is
    0.040 × 0.040 × 0.040
    = $6.4 \times 10^{-5}$ m³ *[1 mark]*
    density = mass ÷ volume
    Rearrange for mass:
    mass = density × volume *[1 mark]*
    = $8800 \times 6.4 \times 10^{-5}$ *[1 mark]*
    = 0.5632 kg
    = 0.56 kg (to 2 s.f.) *[1 mark]*

### Test 16 — Pages 32–33

1. C *[1 mark]*  2. B *[1 mark]*
3. C *[1 mark]*  4. C *[1 mark]*
5. A *[1 mark]*  6. A *[1 mark]*
7. B *[1 mark]*  8. C *[1 mark]*
9. An increase in the amount of energy in the kinetic energy stores of the gas particles leads to an increase in their average velocity *[1 mark]*, and so they collide with the walls of their container with greater force/harder and more frequently *[1 mark]*.
10. pressure due to a column of liquid = height of column × density of liquid × gravitational field strength
    or $P = h \times \rho \times g$ *[1 mark]*
    = 0.82 × 870 × 10 *[1 mark]*
    = 7134 Pa (or 7100 Pa to 2 s.f.) *[1 mark]*
11. 500 g = 0.5 kg
    change in thermal energy
    = 0.5 × 390 × 15 *[1 mark]*
    = 2925 J
    (or 3000 J to 1 s.f.)
    *[1 mark]*

## Section 6 — Magnetism and Electromagnetism

### Test 17 — Pages 34–35

1. C *[1 mark]*  2. B *[1 mark]*
3. B *[1 mark]*  4. C *[1 mark]*
5. A *[1 mark]*  6. B *[1 mark]*
7. A *[1 mark]*  8. C *[1 mark]*
9. Anticlockwise *[1 mark]*.
   (To work this out, choose a side of the coil and then use the left-hand rule. Remember, magnetic fields go from north to south.)
10. E.g. the a.c. electrical signals travel through a coil of wire in the loudspeaker, which is wrapped around the base of a cone *[1 mark]*. The coil is surrounded by a permanent magnet, so the a.c. signals cause a varying force on the coil, making it move back and forth *[1 mark]*. These movements make the cone vibrate, producing sound waves *[1 mark]*.
11. input power = output power
    or $V_p I_p = V_s I_s$ *[1 mark]*
    Rearrange for $I_p$:
    $I_p = \dfrac{V_s I_s}{V_p}$
    $= \dfrac{450\,000 \times 0.018}{230}$ *[1 mark]*
    = 35.2... = 35 A (to 2 s.f.) *[1 mark]*

### Test 18 — Pages 36–37

1. B *[1 mark]*  2. B *[1 mark]*
3. A *[1 mark]*  4. C *[1 mark]*
5. C *[1 mark]*  6. A *[1 mark]*
7. A *[1 mark]*  8. B *[1 mark]*
9.

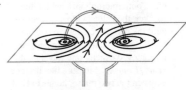

*[1 mark for drawing correct pattern, 1 mark for arrows pointing in the correct directions]*

10. N *[1 mark]*. The left-hand rule shows that the field goes from right to left so ? must be a north pole *[1 mark]*.
11. By increasing the strength of the magnet *[1 mark]*, increasing the number of turns on the coil *[1 mark]* and by increasing the speed of the rotation *[1 mark]*.

# Answers

## Section 7 — Radioactivity and Particles

### Test 19 — Pages 38–39

1.  C *[1 mark]*          2.  A *[1 mark]*
3.  C *[1 mark]*          4.  C *[1 mark]*
5.  A *[1 mark]*          6.  B *[1 mark]*
7.  C *[1 mark]*          8.  B *[1 mark]*
9.  E.g. substances on Earth (e.g. air, food, building materials, soil, rocks) / radiation from space (cosmic rays) / living things / radiation due to human activity (e.g. fallout from nuclear explosions or nuclear waste from power stations) *[1 mark]*
10. Radiation can cause mutations in living organisms *[1 mark]*. Radiation can damage/kill cells and tissue *[1 mark]*.
11. $^{241}_{95}\text{Am} \rightarrow ^{237}_{93}\text{Np} + ^{4}_{2}\text{He}$
    *[1 mark for correct mass number and 1 mark for correct atomic number.]*
12. Half-life = 4 hours
    *[2 marks for a correct answer, otherwise 1 mark for an attempt to find the half-life using a correct method.]*

### Test 20 — Pages 40–41

1.  B *[1 mark]*          2.  A *[1 mark]*
3.  A *[1 mark]*          4.  C *[1 mark]*
5.  C *[1 mark]*          6.  A *[1 mark]*
7.  B *[1 mark]*          8.  B *[1 mark]*
9.  16 *[1 mark]*
10. E.g. if the count-rate reduces significantly when the paper is used, then the source emits alpha radiation *[1 mark]*. If the count rate is greatly reduced by the aluminium but not the paper, then the source emits beta radiation *[1 mark]*. If the count rate isn't greatly reduced by either sheet then the source emits gamma radiation *[1 mark]*.
11. When a nuclear fission reaction occurs, a number of neutrons are emitted *[1 mark]*. These neutrons can be absorbed by other nuclei *[1 mark]* and trigger other nuclear fission reactions that also release neutrons, causing a chain reaction *[1 mark]*.

## Section 8 — Astrophysics

### Test 21 — Pages 42–43

1.  B *[1 mark]*          2.  C *[1 mark]*
3.  C *[1 mark]*          4.  A *[1 mark]*
5.  A *[1 mark]*          6.  B *[1 mark]*
7.  B *[1 mark]*          8.  A *[1 mark]*

9.  The time period is the time taken for the satellite to orbit the Earth once.
    orbital radius = 42 000 km
    = 42 000 000 m *[1 mark]*
    $$\text{orbital speed} = \frac{2 \times \pi \times \text{orbital radius}}{\text{time period}}$$
    rearranges to give:
    $$\text{time period} = \frac{2 \times \pi \times \text{orbital radius}}{\text{orbital speed}}$$
    $$\text{time period} = \frac{2 \times \pi \times 42\,000\,000}{3050}$$
    *[1 mark]*
    time period = 86 522.5... s
    = 87 000 s (to 2 s.f.)
    *[1 mark]*
10. When the light from a galaxy is red-shifted, it suggests that the galaxy is moving away from us *[1 mark]*. Red-shift measurements indicate that distant galaxies are moving away from us in all directions *[1 mark]*. More distant galaxies have greater red-shifts than closer ones, indicating that they are moving away faster than closer galaxies *[1 mark]*. This indicates that the whole universe is expanding. *[1 mark]*.

### Test 22 — Pages 44–45

1.  A *[1 mark]*          2.  A *[1 mark]*
3.  C *[1 mark]*          4.  B *[1 mark]*
5.  B *[1 mark]*          6.  C *[1 mark]*
7.  B *[1 mark]*          8.  C *[1 mark]*
9.  A = nebula *[1 mark]*
    B = white dwarf *[1 mark]*
10. The supply of hydrogen in the star's core, which is the fuel for nuclear fusion, runs out / Fusion ends, meaning that the outward pressure no longer balances the gravitational force *[1 mark]*.
11. The wavelength of the light emitted by the galaxy is known as the reference wavelength.
    change in wavelength = $\Delta\lambda$
    reference wavelength = $\lambda_0$
    velocity of a galaxy = $v$
    speed of light = $c$
    So $\dfrac{\Delta\lambda}{\lambda_0} = \dfrac{v}{c}$.
    $\Delta\lambda$ = 72 nm = $7.2 \times 10^{-8}$ m *[1 mark]*
    Rearrange the equation for $\lambda_0$ and substitute in the values:
    $$\lambda_0 = \frac{\Delta\lambda \times c}{v} \quad \textit{[1 mark]}$$
    $$= \frac{7.2 \times 10^{-8} \times 3.00 \times 10^8}{4.5 \times 10^7} \quad \textit{[1 mark]}$$
    $= 4.8 \times 10^{-7}$ m *[1 mark]*

## Mixed Tests for Paper 1

### Test 23 — Pages 46–47

1.  B *[1 mark]*          2.  B *[1 mark]*
3.  B *[1 mark]*          4.  C *[1 mark]*
5.  B *[1 mark]*          6.  A *[1 mark]*
7.  C *[1 mark]*          8.  B *[1 mark]*
9.  change in $x = 11 - 4 = 7$
    change in $y = 27 - 18 = 9$ *[1 mark]*
    For uniform acceleration,
    acceleration = gradient
    $= 9 \div 7$ *[1 mark]*
    $= 1.285...$ *[1 mark]*
    $= 1.3$ m/s² (to 2 s.f.) *[1 mark]*
10. Total circuit resistance
    $= 2.0 + 3.0 = 5.0\ \Omega$ *[1 mark]*
    Rearrange $V = I \times R$ for $I$:
    $I = V \div R = 9.3 \div 5.0$ *[1 mark]*
    $= 1.86$ A
    $= 1.9$ A (to 2 s.f.) *[1 mark]*

### Test 24 — Pages 48–49

1.  C *[1 mark]*          2.  B *[1 mark]*
3.  A *[1 mark]*          4.  C *[1 mark]*
5.  B *[1 mark]*          6.  A *[1 mark]*
7.  C *[1 mark]*          8.  A *[1 mark]*
9.  There are initially 14 000 radioactive nuclei, so after one half-life there will be 7000 radioactive nuclei. *[1 mark]*
    Reading from graph:
    half-life = $5.6 \times 10^3$ years *[1 mark]*
    $16.8 \times 10^3$ years is
    $(16.8 \times 10^3) \div (5.6 \times 10^3)$
    = 3 half-lives *[1 mark]*
    Number of radioactive nuclei left after 2 half-lives = 7000 ÷ 2 = 3500
    Number of radioactive nuclei left after 3 half-lives
    = 3500 ÷ 2 = 1750 *[1 mark]*
10. efficiency = (useful energy output ÷ total energy output) × 100 *[1 mark]*
    Rearrange the equation:
    useful energy output
    = efficiency ÷ 100 × total energy output
    = 75 ÷ 100 × 560 *[1 mark]*
    = 420 J *[1 mark]*

# Answers

## Test 25 — Pages 50–51

1. B *[1 mark]*  2. A *[1 mark]*
3. C *[1 mark]*  4. C *[1 mark]*
5. B *[1 mark]*  6. B *[1 mark]*
7. A *[1 mark]*  8. B *[1 mark]*
9. The Doppler effect *[1 mark]*. The motion of the ambulance away from the observer stretches the wavelength of the sound waves, which lowers their frequency *[1 mark]*.
10. The current in the resistor causes energy to be transferred electrically *[1 mark]*. This causes a rise in temperature / The energy is then transferred by heating to the bread *[1 mark]*.
11. The distance is equal to the area under the graph. Area under the graph from 0 s to 10 s is:
$0.5 \times 10 \times 80 = 400$ m *[1 mark]*
and area from 10 s to 15 s is
$5 \times 80 = 400$ m *[1 mark]*
so the distance travelled is
$400 + 400 = 800$ m *[1 mark]*

## Test 26 — Pages 52–53

1. C *[1 mark]*  2. C *[1 mark]*
3. C *[1 mark]*  4. A *[1 mark]*
5. A *[1 mark]*  6. A *[1 mark]*
7. A *[1 mark]*  8. C *[1 mark]*
9. In a series circuit, the supply voltage is shared, so:
$V_3 = V_1 + V_2 = 3 + 2 = 5$ V *[1 mark]*
Resistances add up, so:
$R = R_1 + R_2 = 6 + 4 = 10 \ \Omega$ *[1 mark]*
The ammeter will measure the total current. The current can be calculated using the supply voltage and the total resistance of the circuit. (Alternatively, it could be calculated using the voltage across $R_1$ or $R_2$.)
voltage = current × resistance
or $V = I \times R$
Rearrange the formula:
$I = V \div R$
$= V_3 \div R$
$= 5 \div 10$ *[1 mark]*
$= 0.5$ A *[1 mark]*
10. (final speed)² = (initial speed)²
+ (2 × acceleration × distance)
or $v^2 = u^2 + (2 \times a \times s)$
Rearrange for $u^2$:
$u^2 = v^2 - (2 \times a \times s)$
Then
$u = \sqrt{v^2 - (2 \times a \times s)}$ *[1 mark]*
$= \sqrt{13.6^2 - (2 \times 2.50 \times 14.0)}$ *[1 mark]*
$= 10.721... = 10.7$ m/s (to 3 s.f.) *[1 mark]*

## Mixed Tests for Paper 2

### Test 27 — Pages 54–55

1. B *[1 mark]*  2. A *[1 mark]*
3. C *[1 mark]*  4. B *[1 mark]*
5. C *[1 mark]*  6. A *[1 mark]*
7. C *[1 mark]*  8. B *[1 mark]*
9. The first peak is at 0.01 s and the second peak is at 0.035 s, so:
period = 0.035 − 0.01
$= 0.025$ s *[1 mark]*
frequency = 1 ÷ period
$= 1 \div 0.025$ *[1 mark]*
$= 40$ Hz *[1 mark]*
*[Or 3 marks for the correct answer via any other method.]*
10.

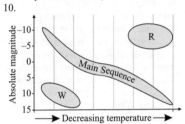

*[1 mark for area where white dwarfs can be found marked approximately correctly and labelled W, 1 mark for area where red giants and supergiants can be found marked approximately correctly and labelled R]*
11. Block C *[1 mark]*, as it has the lowest temperature change for the given amount of energy supplied, so it must take the most energy to increase its temperature by 1 °C *[1 mark]*.

### Test 28 — Pages 56–57

1. B *[1 mark]*  2. A *[1 mark]*
3. C *[1 mark]*  4. A *[1 mark]*
5. A *[1 mark]*  6. B *[1 mark]*
7. C *[1 mark]*  8. B *[1 mark]*
9. $V_P I_P = V_S I_S$ *[1 mark]*
Rearrange for $I_S$:
$I_S = (V_P I_P) \div V_S$ *[1 mark]*
$= (54.0 \times 8.00) \div 32.0$
$= 13.5$ A *[1 mark]*
10. clockwise moment around B = anticlockwise moment around B
$T_A \times 10 = 560 \times 2.5$ *[1 mark]*
$T_A = (560 \times 2.5) \div 10 = 140$ N *[1 mark]*
$T_A + T_B = 560$ N *[1 mark]*
$T_B = 560 - 140 = 420$ N *[1 mark]*
*[Or 4 marks for the correct answers via any other method.]*

## Test 29 — Pages 58–59

1. A *[1 mark]*  2. A *[1 mark]*
3. C *[1 mark]*  4. A *[1 mark]*
5. B *[1 mark]*  6. C *[1 mark]*
7. B *[1 mark]*  8. A *[1 mark]*
9. Transformers *[1 mark]*. Transformers are used to increase the voltage and decrease the current of electricity for energy-efficient transmission *[1 mark]*. They are then used to reduce the voltage to a safe, usable level when it reaches consumers *[1 mark]*.
10. Total momentum before collision = total momentum after collision *[1 mark]*
Bullet momentum = mass × momentum
$= 0.1 \times 100 = 10$ kg m/s *[1 mark]*
So gun's momentum is −10 kg m/s.
Rearrange the formula:
velocity = momentum ÷ mass
$= -10 \div 2$ *[1 mark]*
$= -5$ m/s
So recoil speed is 5 m/s *[1 mark]*.
*[Or 4 marks for the correct answer via any other method.]*

## Test 30 — Pages 60–61

1. A *[1 mark]*  2. A *[1 mark]*
3. B *[1 mark]*  4. A *[1 mark]*
5. C *[1 mark]*  6. B *[1 mark]*
7. A *[1 mark]*  8. B *[1 mark]*
9. E.g. radioactive waste is produced which is difficult to dispose of safely. / It's expensive to set up and close down nuclear power stations. / There is a risk of radiation leaks and catastrophes. *[1 mark]*
10. $n = \dfrac{\sin i}{\sin r} = \dfrac{\sin 54}{\sin 33}$ *[1 mark]*
$= 1.485...$ *[1 mark]*
$= 1.5$ (to 2 s.f.) *[1 mark]*
11. $\dfrac{\text{change in wavelength}}{\text{reference wavelength}}$
$= \dfrac{\text{velocity of a galaxy}}{\text{speed of light}}$
Or $\dfrac{\lambda - \lambda_0}{\lambda_0} = \dfrac{v}{c}$
Rearrange for $v$:
$v = c \times \left( \dfrac{\lambda - \lambda_0}{\lambda_0} \right)$ *[1 mark]*
$= (3.00 \times 10^8) \times$
$\dfrac{(6.21 \times 10^{-7}) - (5.75 \times 10^{-7})}{(5.75 \times 10^{-7})}$
*[1 mark]*
$= 24\ 000\ 000$ m/s
(or $2.4 \times 10^7$ m/s) *[1 mark]*

PFYP1A1